Curry and Rice

Curry and Rice

The Ingredients of Social Life
at
"Our Station" in India

George Francklin Atkinson

Rupa & Co
__DAKSHIN__

Published by

Rupa . Co
DAKSHIN

36, Kutty Street, Nungambakkam, Chennai 600 034
Surya Shree, B-6, New 66, Shankara Park,
Basavangudi, Bangalore 560 004
3-5-612, Himayat Nagar, Hyderabad 500 029

ISBN 81-7167-573-5

Typeset Copyright © Rupa & Co., DAKSHIN 2001

Typeset by
Nikita Overseas Pvt Ltd, 19-A Ansari Road, New Delhi 110 002

Printed in India by
Rekha Printers Pvt Ltd, A-102/1 Okhla Industrial Area, Phase-II
New Delhi-110 020

Contents

Our Station 1

Our Judge 5

Our Judge's Wife 8

Our Magistrate 12

Our Magistrate's Wife 16

Our Colonel 20

Our Colonel's Wife 24

Our Padre 28

Our Joint Magistrate and Collector 33

Our Mall 37

Our German Missionary 41

Our Doctor 45

Our Doctor's Wife 49

Our Invalid Major 53

Our Spins 57

Our Band 61

Our Races 65

Our Coffee-Shop 69

Our Bath	73
Our Sporting Griff	77
Our Moonshee	81
Our Burra Khanah	85
Our Pack of Hounds	89
Our Ball	93
Our Tiger-Shooting	97
Our Stage-Coaching	101
Our Agriculturists	105
Our Nuwab	109
Our Theatricals	113
Our Bazar	117
Our Bed Room	120
Our Travellers Bungalow	124
Our Cook Room	128
Our Cloth Merchants	132
Our Pig-Sticking	136
Our Garden	140
Our Farm Yard	144
Our Wedding	148
Our Departure for Home	152

Preface

Gentle Reader

Before you can be landed on the sunny shores of Ind, a tedious voyage must be overcome. Before you are transported into the scenes depicted in the following pages, a preliminary voyage, in the way of a Preface, has to be encountered. Allow me, then, to improve the occasion by a few sober words of exhortation, that I may dissipate at one and for ever some of those fallacious opinions and crude notions that you persist in entertaining regarding that land called "India."

Allow me, first, to impress upon you this geographical fact, that India is about the size of all Europe. The British possessions are subdivided into distinct governments, each a kingdom in itself. Bengal, Madras, and Bombay are as different and far more disconnected than are England, Ireland, and Scotland. That eccentric idea, that floats so persistently in your imagination, of jumping to the conclusion that because dear Charley is going to India, he must infallibly meet dear Willy, who is already there, is slightly illogical. For dear

Willy, if I mistake not, belongs to the Bengal Presidency, and is stationed at the very North-west boundary of the empire, at the foot of the Himalayas, close to Cashmere; while dear Charley is bound for Madras, and you may probably hear from him at Cape Comorin, when there will be *only* the trifling intervening distance of some 2,000 miles between them.

You might equally well hope that your travelling cousin Alex, who is going to fish in Norway, must be sure to see your dear cousin Maria, who is scrambling about the ruins of the Parthenon; or that because the aforesaid migratory Alex is going to St. Petersburg, he will need a letter of introduction to General Friskhimoff, the Military Governor of Eastern Siberia.

Secondly—let me remind you that, while there are numerous races with a different creed, caste, and language, so there are customs and manners peculiar to each. This variety is not confined to the natives; for the habits and customs of social life among the English in India likewise present their petty diversities. The "Qui Hye" of Bengal, the "Mull" of Madras, and the "Duck" of Bombay, adhere to and defend their own customs with jealous warmth of feeling. In the following pages, it must be explained, the scenes are drawn to exhibit the customs of society on the Bengal side, as it was necessary throughout to adhere to some one character of people among whom the English were located. But they are such as are common to the whole of India, judging from personal experience in the three Presidencies. And this brings me to the last point upon which I would wish to say a few words.

Among mankind, the perfect individual affords no scope for the exercise of humour. Perfection has nothing comic in it whatsoever. It is only as perfection is deviated from that the victim becomes the object of wit or a shaft for ridicule. Just as a sound and well-constructed wheel, that revolves smoothly on its axle, has nothing in it to excite observation; but when that wheel rotates in a grotesque fashion, symptomatic of immediate aberration from its axle, and, moreover, rattles profusely, it then becomes an object of attraction, and is apt to create a smile.

Those, then, of my readers, who imagine that I have singled out the faults and absurdities of our race, will perhaps, accept as my reason for so doing. My object was not to illustrate perfection, but to afford amusement, by dwelling upon the sunny side of Indian life, after all the narratives of horror that have of late fallen upon the English ear. But I wish it to be distinctly known that no living mortals have been taken as models for the pictures here drawn, and that if there are any sensitive beings who will fit the cap on their own heads, I can only say that it is their own doing, and not mine.

And now, having brought you so far on your voyage, with the comforting assurance that you are not the persons "so cruelly handed up," let me land you in the East, where you will receive a warm welcome most assuredly. That you may experience a pleasant time of it during your visit at "Our Station." I indulge a hope. And if in the Plates "Curry and Rice," now set before you, the flavour is found to be a little too spicy and a little too pungent, and, to many perhaps, a thought too hot, remember that it is the nature of Curry to be so. Trusting, however, that it will prove to be a dish to your liking, and leaving you alone to partake of it, and I hope enjoy it!

G. F. ATKINSON

WHAT varied opinions we constantly hear
　　Of our rich Oriental possessions;
What a jumble of notions, distorted and queer,
　　From an Englishman's "Indian impressions!"

First a sun, fierce and glaring, that scorches and bakes;
　　Palankeens, perspiration, and worry;
Mosquitoes, thugs, cocoa-nuts, Brahmins, and snakes,
　　With elephants, tigers, and Curry.

Them Juggernât, punkahs, tanks, buffaloes, forts,
　　With bangles, mosques, nautches, and dhingees;
A mixture of temples, Mahometans, ghâts,
　　With scorpions, Hindoos, and Feringhees.

Then jungles, fakeers, dancing-girls, prickly heat,
　　Shawls, idols, durbars, brandy-pawny;
Rupees, clever jugglers, dust-storms, slipper'd feet,
　　Rainy season, and mulligatawny.

Hot winds, holy monkey, tall minarets, Rice,
　　With crocodiles, ryots or farmers;
Himalayas, fat baboos, with paunches and pice,
　　So airily clad in pyjamas.

With Rajahas —But stop, I must really desist,
　　And let each one enjoy his opinions,
Whilst I show in what style Anglo-Indians exist
　　In her Majesty's Eastern dominions.

CURRY & RICE

OUR STATION

OUR JUDGE

Page No. 5

OUR JUDGE'S WIFE

Page No.

Our Station

"Our Station" rejoices in the euphonious appellation of Kabob. It is situated in the plains of Dekchy, in the province of Bobarchy. Far from the busy haunts of a civilized world, and the traffickings of men, and plunged in wild retirement of a luxuriant jungle, smiles Kabob, "the loveliest village of the plain," basking beneath the rays of the orient sun. Oh! if there be a paradise upon earth, I suspect it must be this!

The general aspect of Kabob is obtrusively prepossessing. It is bounded on the north and east by a mountainous range of flaming brick-kilns, whilst on the south and west it is embraced in the tortuous sinuosities of a circumambient ravine populous with pigs. But Kabob—and the truth must be told outright—Kabob is not regarded in the light of being the most attractive station in India. Popular prejudice protests against its secluded locality, and malignant slander whispers, in no faint accents, that a hotter and a duller hole is not to be discovered by the most enterprising and enthusiastic tropical traveller—

"Remote, unfriended, melancholy, slow."

To be sure, and we must confess it, Kabob is not the capital of the province. The councillors of the kingdom, the great men and the mighty men, do not reside here, nor do the high Church dignitaries, nor any military magnate, not even a general. Then, again, it is not situated on the banks of the holy Gunga; its solitary temple is not reflected in the bosom of that sacred and budgerow-bearing river. Nor, again, do its stately dwellings and lofty palm-trees grace the skirts of the Grand Portmanteau Road that intersects the Northern Empire. Steamers do not furrow the waters that flow by its sunburnt banks, dropping as they pass their timely offerings of Allsop and of Bass. Nor does the shrill whistle and intermittent puff of the locomotive "molest its ancient solitary reign." But what of that? Have not the works of the Great Lohar Railroad been commenced upon? Have not the great capitalists of Kabob-the princes, the governors, the captains, the judges, and all the rest of them-taken shares? and does not every one know that in twenty years' time the line will be open, and that Kabob will then be within one hundred and fifty miles only of the nearest point on the line? Ha! ha! What can scandal say then? Kabob will be isolated no more-benighted no longer. We see it all. The once dim future is now a very meridian blaze of brightness. We see with a distinct vision consignments of bitter beer pouring into our rugged highways. No longer shall the anxious bullock yield his last breath in glorious but unavailing efforts to drag the much-expected load of six dozen chests. The wild tracks shall no longer be made known by the whitened bones which there unburied shine, and tell the startling tale of supplies for British mouths from Briton's isle drawn ruthlessly over many a hundred miles of bleak expanse.

Away with melancholy, then! for Kabob, let me tell you, will be, moreover, a thoroughfare to the lands of the West, when the Great Lohar line is open. Visions haunt me of travellers thronging to our portals-blue—eyed young maidens fresh from dear England and blear-eyed old Indians, belivered and bedevilled, on their way to England. Visions of claret and Allsop, of choicest delicacies hermetically sealed—all at a reduced tariff. O Kabob! Enviable Kabob, what greatness is in store for thee!

But let us stray through thy sandy meadows and grass-grown streets, fair Kabob! and tell of all thy architectural splendours, thy accumulated glories of whitewash and of thatch, thy mud-built edifices and thy mud-built cottages, thy mud-built enclosure walls, in all their mud-begotten majesty!

Ah! there is the parade-ground. There, on that bare and barren plain, do our dusky Trojans learn the art of war. There the embryo hero rises from the pristine performance of the goose-step to a full knowledge of brigade manœuvres. In order that Kabob may enjoy the full benefit of the westerly breezes-which in summer, let me tell you, blow with summary and unquenchable fury, but which, nevertheless, are highly appreciated. "Our Station," as usual, faces the west. On the eastern side, then, of the Parade are the "Lines." First, is a row of apparently magnified sentry-boxes, commonly called Bells of Arms, which appellation denotes their object. In rear of these are the huts for the native troops—small mud-wall tenements roofed with thatch, amidst rows of sickly plantains.

Immediately behind these are the domiciles for the officers, in two or more lines—each dwelling, commonly yclept a bungalow, in its own peculiar territory, which varies in dimensions, as orthodoxy had originally designed it, under the fond but fanciful delusion that subalterns had small and field officers great requirements. These bungalows, you observe, look like exaggerated beehives, perched upon mile-stones—a judicious combination of mud, whitewash, and thatch. We will go into one presently. Let us now see only the outer life of Kabob. There, that square whitewashed edifice, with an excrescence at one end, looking for all the world like an extinguisher on a three-dozen chest!-what is it? You may well ask. It is the church! A regular protestant building against everything architectural, æsthetic, ornamental, or useful; designed and built according to a Government prescription. Next to it is our assembly-room and theatre. Just beyond you see the hospitals, then comes the racket-court, and to the left is the well-stocked burial-ground. This is the course, where the live splendour of Kabob resort when shades of evening close upon us. There is the band-stand, and this is the station bath. On the extreme right are the barracks, for you must know that Europeans man the guns of our battery that is quartered here. That is the artillery-mess, and opposite lives Stickerdoss, who sells European goods and can accommodate you with anything, from a baby's bottle to a bolster.

Now we must turn to the left, and verging from the confines of the military cantonment, we plunge onto territory that is under civil sway. These are the civil lines. Those flat-roofed edifices in the Brummagem Tuscan order, all pillars, plaster, and pea-green paint, are the courts of law. This shed is the treasury, and those men guarding it are Our Magistrate's own peculiars. This piece of ground, with its five cabbages, three peach-trees, and patch of onions, is the Government Botanical Garden and, on your right and left, those wide-verandahed habitations are the dwelling-places of the civilians.

And now, as the sun is getting piping hot, let us gallop home. After breakfast we will make a day of it, and you shall be introduced to all the beauty and fashion of "Our Station."

Our Judge

$\mathcal{I}$ must introduce you to Turmeric. He is "Our Judge" — a tremendous dignitary! right at the top of the social tree of Our Station, but so desperately absorbed with his official duties, that we see but little of him. His judicial soul being so saturated with appeals, criminal cases, decrees, circular order, and the like, that when we do meet, the theme of his discourse is so potently flavoured with law, we are overwhelmed with references to Act 95 of 17, Regulation 11 of 78, or some such frightful numbers, which are about as intelligible to us as the the hieroglyphics of Nineveh. Who cares for Act 95 of 17, I should like to know?

There you see him in his court—niggers—ten thousand pardons! no, not niggers, I mean natives—sons of the soil—Orientals—Asiatics, are his source of happiness. And there, penned up in that stifling enclosure from "rosy morn, to stewy eve," does he vegetate, surrounded by his jabbering myrmidons. In external man "Our Judge" is suggestive of a boiled bamboo, and in his style of apparel there is presumptive evidence of its being home-made. It is clear that he is no longer—as when a gay Lothario at Calcutta—heedful of the vanities of dress, for he is addicted to the white jacket of a bygone cycle, and appears to encourage the hiatus that exists between it and its nether continuation. These invariably fail to extend to the vicinity of his shoes, which, built after an ancient model, are prodigal in bows.

For thirty and two years uninterruptedly has "Our Judge" been parboiling in India, nor can he be persuaded to turn his steps to old England, of which country his notions are somewhat opaque. I have a faint idea he hopes to get into Council, and prefers an official life for his declining day, to idleness in obscure retirement. To him, modern England has no luring attractiveness. In his estimation, life in London involves a residence in small, dark rooms and that to stare out of window at the rain, is one's only solace and delight, whilst a country life consists in vegetating with cows and corn, in ignoble obscurity. These, coupled with the necessary perquisites of colds, coughs, umbrellas, sore throats, chilblains, draughts, chest complaints, and such-like, disincline "Our Judge" from returning to the land of his fathers. In private life "Our Judge" is musical. He operates upon the violoncello, and a great adept at the fiddle and the bow is "Our Judge." What our musical *soirées* would be without him is a problem that remains to be solved, for the violoncello, accompanied by its rightful owner, is invariably to be found at every party—a regular standing dish! Turmeric himself gives ornamental tea-parties for the furtherance of harmony on a large and enjoyment on a small scale. For who could be such a heathen as even to whisper during the perpetration of a piece of Mozart's some five and forty pages in length, even if silence was not enforced by the fair Mrs. Turmeric, whose admonition, conveyed in terrible frowns, combined with telegraphic signals of a manual nature, is wonderfully efficacious as an antidote to loquacity.

Mrs. Turmeric play? — Not she. She has as much idea of a piano as of the sack but, psaltery, dulcimer, or any other kind of musical instrument. Turmeric, Mrs. Capsicum, Cheeny, and Pullow form the standing quartette, and great are the practisings which periodically occur. And if Pullow was only a little less asthmatic, and Mrs. Capsicum would not pound so much, or Turmetic plunge down to such awful depths with his bass at inappropriate periods, the effect would be transcendentally sweet. As it is, Pullow swears that Turmeric never keeps time. Cheeny, as he lights his parting cheroot, vows that Mother Capsy puts him out with her confounded "one, two, three, four—one, two, three, four," that she counts out aloud. And Turmeric gets all abroad with his quavers, at Cheeny interpolating unjustifiable variations on his violin, and gets so confused that he begins alluding to Regulation 54 of 99 on the spot. As for Mrs. Capsicum, she tells me, in strict confidence, that that odious Major Pullow never will let her finish a bar, but poo-poos off most unpremeditately, as if he couldn't help it.

But it all tends to promote sociability, which Turmeric loves in his quiet way. He is hospitable to a degree; his house, never without its visitors, is a perfect travellers' home, and, morever, his table, which is often spread, is by no means a *terra incog.* to subalterns, to whom he gives a friendly welcome. Altogether, "Our judge" is decidedly popular, and his departure from Kabob would be much felt by every one at "Our Station."

Our Judge's Wife

*B*ut you really must call upon Mrs. Turmeric. She is the Burra *Beebee*, the great lady of Kabob; and I am inclined to think she is not entirely unconscious of the dignity of her state in life. For when Lord Tamarind, on his Eastern travels, passed through Kabob, and handed Mrs. Chutney in to dinner, great was the indignation in the Turmeric bosom. I would recommend your not alluding to the peerage, or you will infallibly be inflicted with a detailed narrative of the entire proceeding. Mrs. Turmeric is a victim to grief. The world, it would appear, wages a continual warfare with her, and all belonging to her-the greatest grievance being on the state of the Civil Service. She bewails loudly at the cruelty of her husband not being a Commissioner, and avers that it was a most unjustifiable act of aggression that he was superseded, when he ought to be one of the *Suddur*, or, at any rate, the Resident of Horsepore, or Governor-General's Agent at Salaāmabad. And, between ourselves, I suspect she imagines he ought to be Governor-General himself.

A regular perambulating civil-service compendium is Mrs.

Turmeric! Just hear how she Jeremiahs at the slowness of promotion. "Only think," says she. "Hulwer Sone has got into the *Suddur*. He has been popped over the heads of eleven of his seniors-Johnny Kullum goes home, Mr. Kydy has got the Judgeship of Seeipore, and Charley Dufter is to be Collector of Croquetabad. Only think, Pitty Patty,quite a boy, not thirteen years in the service, is to be Commissioner in Hulwer Sone's place. Mr. Lafarfer is appointed Civil Auditor—what will the Shelgums say to this job? Shelgum, who didn't go home last year, expecting to get into the *Suddur* and Mrs. S. just come out from England with all her finery, going to cut such a dash at Atushpore, will have all her silks and satins and feathers destroyed at that wretched Junglabad (and serve her right,—what business had she to go to court!). And all this because Pitty Patty must be provided for. Only think, the Bonus scheme will be knocked on the head. For that odious Currer Row, and Pusund Ney, and others, will not subscribe And there's Johnny Walah offers to go if we will only pay up 15,000 rupees and land him in Bond-street; and there never was such good step as that. And then the annuity business— they want Turmeric to pay Heaven knows how many thousand rupees, because those foolish young boys at college will marry so soon, get such large families, and then die off, leaving us to support the awful arrears to the fund, which cannot exist under such pressure from without."

Such are Mrs. Turmeric's official griefs. She has some also of a domestic nature. "Now this is really too bad," she says; "you see Mrs. McGhee, the Chutneys, Dr. Goley, and ourselves, form a Mutton Club, and we kill a sheep in turn. And it is quite shocking to see the scraggy stuff they send-just like half-starved kid and then they take my beautiful sheep, that have been three years on grain. What's more, when they do give a party, it is sure to be on 'Mrs. Turmeric's killing-day.' I really must speak to Mrs. Chutney. I don't believe she gives a particle of grain all the year round. And as for Mrs. McGhee, she wants to palm off her nasty grass-fed sheep as the best flock in the club."

But, with all her afflictions, the portly frame of "Our Judge's Wife" appears to thrive. It is currently reported that Turmeric's generous hospitality goes sadly against her grain, and that her abilities as a household financier and domestic manager are exquisitely unique—personally supervising with a detective's skill the operations of the kitchen, and not scorning to assist in the manipulation of puddings, pastry, and the like. She is judicious in her selection of a ham, and has a keen eye for a turkey and from her frequent allusions to a continental wine-merchant, we are led to infer that the champagne is not a decoction of gooseberries. Mirrich, who knows everything, positively asseverates that the liquids are purchased from that villain Stickerdoss; that they have been fished out of the Ganges, and subsequently bought at auction. This I suspect must be an erroneous impression; for if you slave to appropriate clandestinely the Judge's private bottle, you'll find it to be of a peculiarly good vintage. Garlic, who was at the coffee-shop this morning (and a shockingly libellous fellow he is, no one can possibly believe him), takes his affidavit that he often sees Mrs. Turmeric wolloping the turkeys, and chevying the fowls, to make them lay eggs. He declares he has seen her in her verandah larruping the goatman with her slipper, because there appeared a deficit in the milk-pail; and Chabook, her coachman, came howling out of the compound-gate the other day with a cuff on his head, for having suggested the propriety of dispensing a little more grain to the horses. Between ourselves, old Capsicum declares that Mrs. Tumeric's sheep are as lean as her husband, and a good deal more tough.

But Mrs. Turmeric is a good old soul, and she would be positively miserable without a grievance and if all things went absolutely smooth. But if she would let off the steam without the addition of the whistle, the explosive matter would escape without it being so generally known throughout the length and breadth of "Our Station."

Our Magistrate

Lord Coriander positively arrived this morning, and Chutney, "Our Magistrate," has secured him. He was bound for Our Judge's hospitable mansion, but Chutney, who patronizes the peerage, and who studied the genealogical tree of the Coriander family down to its very roots, on hearing that Kabob was about to be smiled upon by sprig of aristocracy, lay in wait for his arrival, at a discreet distance from the station, and brought him in, in triumph. Chutney delights in welcoming within his portals the great ones of the land. He has ensnared several mighty men of renown. A governor was once entrapped in his snare, to his unlimited satisfaction; while, last year, he skilfully made capture of a bishop, but for whose appropriation popular rumour avows that he betokened symptoms of repentance. He has secured Lord Coriander, however, who is making the grand tour for the improvement of his individual mind, and the better enlightening of the great House at home on Indian matters. I rather suspect his lordship will be let in for a dose of law, as administered by the functionaries of our Eastern empire.

Settlements, revenues, land, tax, decress, jails, crops, remissions, duties, salt, police, coupled with thannahs, cutcherries, ryotwarry, beegahs, zameendars, chowkees, tuhseels, zillahs, kydees, omlahs, sherishtadars, and many other *dars*, will be fully set before him, to float tumultuously in his bewildered brain at the midnight hour, to the disorderment of his dreams.

Lord Coriander is a captain in the Guards, but his aristocratical superiority cancels this defect in Chutney's eye, for Chutney, let me tell you, looks not with a favouring eye on the brother service. The military are his aversion, being an inferior caste—inferior in emoluments, and in the classified scale of precedence And Chutney is gifted with the excellence of being cast in a nobler mould. "Those people from the barracks" is his appellation for the military, upon whom the glances of his scorn-beaming eye fall witheringly. But Chutney is a zealous, indefatigable magistrate as ever imprisoned a nigger, and the district is ably watched over and cared for under his guidance.

There, at this early hour, you see him listening to the complaint of a

"Wrinkled *Kydy*, grim and thin,"

and directing the operation of metalling the roads and between ourselves, it is marvellous how excellent are the highways in the immediate vicinity of the domestic habitation that grace the civil lines. Somehow or other, we always do manage to observe gangs of prisoners sedulously employed in bettering the condition of what, to our untutored eye, appears to be immaculate in its perfection. We acknowledge that it must be a cheering termination to the niggers-I mean to the Oriental gentlemen-whose duties attract them to Kabob, and who contribute to the repair of the district roads, to find, after an unmerciful jolting over unmended ways, they should be gratified by an easy run at the close of their sufferings.

Only just take a ride with Chutney, and you will be carried off to survey the creations of his skill in the building line, and record your opinion as to the merits of the architectural fancies which he has developed in pure virgin mud—stately structures for the reception of treasure, or the milder tenements of the rural police! Upon bricks and mortar, too, you will be required to pass judgment, and declare your sentiments with regard to an elaborate and important bridge which he has just opened, consisting of no less than five elliptic arches, spanning a tremendous water–course, fully eighteen inches in depth, and seven feet in width–which, between ourselves, old Soorkee, the head mason, designed and built, but which Chutney claims and exhibits as a startling effort of his constructive genius! It really is a fact, that Chutney positively did once design and erect a bridge, at a happy period when the river bed was dry. But the rains set in, and the floods came, and the water, which it was contemplated and designed to get across, most unaccommodatingly declined to pass quietly through the pre-arranged channel, but, with villanous determination, carried away bricks, mortar and all, and lodged them in an adjoining nullah, to the utter dismay of the collector, and the inconvenience of the swiftly-speeding postman, who unconscious of the sudden change in the arrangements,

"With heedless footsteps ran,"

and plunged, bag and all, into the boisterous wave.

In social life, Chutney entertains extensively. And uncommonly pleasant parties he gives, which the extra-intelligent declare are given for the general patronizing effect which they are designed to produce, and for a more effectual exhibition of the silver plate; whilst plausible rumour affirms that Chutney is a victim to his fond wife's love of gaiety and all the other social virtues, and that to her must be imputed all the merits and the multiplicity of the entertainments.

But let Scandal have her fling. If Chutney is himself dull and heavy, his Moselle is sparkling and light; if his aspirations are for the noble and the great, his table displays evidence of the excellent and the good; if he has a leaning to the powerful and the wealthy, his dishes display a leaning to what is savoury and rich; and, if the silver plate is to be gazed upon and admired, it is set before one with delicacies that can be dwelt upon and applauded. And what if he will talk "shop?" — why, there is his agreeable, fun-loving wife, and the fascinating Carry Cinnamon, to counteract the baneful effect! And what if he has not the soul of song, and is about as musical as a hyæna? — his piano is first-rate, and his fair visitors will rouse its brilliant tones, and you yourself may indulge in unlimited sol-fas for the general enlivenment.

Chutney, however, is thoroughly domestic in his sociability. We cannot draw him to the mess, or to balls, or to the convivialities of the cantonments. But his own house, allowing that it is the fair wife's doing, is ever open, and his mahogany is always well furnished with guests. So we look upon it that he is, unquestionably, one of the greatest promoters of sociability at "Our Station."

Our Magistrate's Wife

Who is that skimpy little woman over there, with fawn-coloured hair and a complexion like curd soap? Why, that is Mrs. Chutney, wife of Maximilian Adolphus Fitznoodle Chutney, B.C.S., Our Magistrate and Collector. She is the niece of the late Lieutenant-General Sir Jeremiah Qui-Hye, K.C.B., a parchment-faced, purple-nosed, patriarchal veteran of the old school, who, when he retired from the service to wreathe his laurels at Kabob, and before he shuffled off this mortal coil, which event took place last year, imported Mrs. Chutney on connubial spec. But she hung fire as an unprofitable investment for many a long and weary day, till she manœuvred Fitznoodle in the meshes of matrimony, and secured the "£300 a year, dead or alive," of the enamoured civilian.

She has got no family, and hates children, of course; but she cultivates pets, and the society of handsome Subs, and, with her, nothing is so charming as to have a lapful of spaniels and a train of A.D.C.'s. Little Charley Bhooker is a huge favourite, while as for Joey Choosner, he is her established

OUR MAGISTRATE Page No. 12

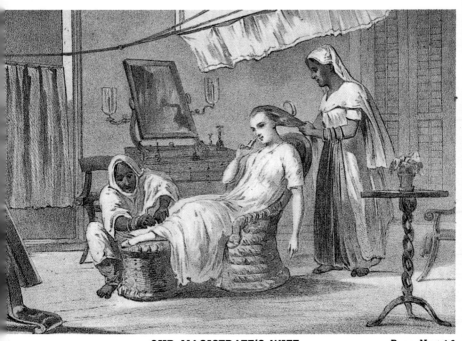

OUR MAGISTRATE'S WIFE Page No. 16

OUR COLONEL

Page No. 2

OUR COLONEL'S WIFE

Page No. 2

satellite, You always see a dozen of her boys, as she calls them, embroidering her carriage at the Band. To be sure, Carry Cinnamon is living with Mrs. Chutney, and unprincipled people insinuate that *there* lies the attraction, and that the bi-weekly feeds are political. But this must be malice, hatred, and all uncharitableness. For Mrs. Chutney is positively *so* engaging, so disinterested, and so winning in her ways and then she gives such delightful dinner-parties.

Mrs. Chutney sing? I should think so—first rate. When she was at the Presidency she took six lessons from Signora Jyfulini. By the way, Signora Jyfulini is daughter of Rosario Lipsalvo, who is a Portuguese, and her mother is as black as my hat. She married Jyful, the bailiff, and having a voice, comes the Italian singer. First she tried in character, but her shady face under a wreath of white roses, looking like Othello in his nightcap, failed to embellish the performance and so she has subsequently subsided into the drawing-room singing mistress and concert amateur.

Well, Mrs. Chutney (who, they say, has got a beautiful voice-to me like a creaking cartwheel under a heavy load-but I am no judge) learnt an Italian song, the words of which she pronounces Anglicè. It is a song you will, of course, hear. It is a standing party song—everybody knows it now. Even Kuddoo, who doesn't recognize the "Evening Hymn" from "The Last Rose of Summer," has been heard to whistle the air as rendered by the pupil of Signora Jyfulini.

Mrs. Chutney has good eyelashes and now is the grand opportunity for a display of the same: back goes the head-down go the eyelids-out go the lashes—the telling note swells and subsides—a shake of the head ensues, and two little syllables, *"a me,"* are daintialy popped out—and all is over. We are credibly informed that she has expressed an urgent desire to be remembered—a request which we are all very likely to vouchsafe.

In consequence of her vocal accomplishments, Mrs. Chutney is one of the choir at Our Church, and plays the seraphine (which Mrs. Chupatty persists in calling a *seraphim*). An asthmatic, wheezy, whining, lugubrious apparatus it is, which moans, and gasps, and squeaks for breath so very inopportunely during the execution of our spiritual songs, that the general effect is anything but solemn. But discord is not confined to the unhappy instrument — the fair choristers are frightfully at variance in the matter of tunes. Mrs. Chutney and her party abjure the Gregorian chants, preferring the modern tunes, which their adversaries call "operatic airs" and so the contention waxes warm. But Mrs. Chutney's party, being in power, has carried the day. Piercing and quavering are the leading notes that come floating from behind that red curtain into the ears of the congregation. And I must say, that, amidst their minor rivalries, the fair choristers do combine most strenuously and effectively in their efforts to "give tongue", resulting in a volume of sound which, if not altogether productive of harmony, threatens by its impressiveness to fracture the congregational tympanum. They do say that the competition behind that red curtain is terrific, each vocalist concentrating her energies to make her individual voice singularly and audibly conspicuous, with view to annihilate and extinguish every sound that proceeds from each and every rival thorax; whence fearful jealousies and hideous shrieks of defiant melody are engendered, Mrs. McGhee volunteered to assist in swelling the tuneful lay by lifting up her voice too in that red-curtained retreat But as the terrible jar occasioned thereby loosened all the back teeth of the entire congregation, and as the volume of sound that escaped from the great cantatrice completely overpowered the voice of the prima donna, Mrs. Chutney, she was delicately solicited to become scarce; and so, out of spite, she sings away most lustily and out of tune in her own pew.

I am not quite sure whether the A.D.C.'s or the choir, or the bi-weekly dinner parties or the family pets, mostly enliven Mrs. Chutney's wearied hour. But I suspect the squirrels and the Persian cats, the cockatoos and the canaries, the minahs and mongooses, and the pigeons and the poodles, appropriate the largest share of her devotion. As for the dogs, nursed in the lap of luxury and of their mistress, they excite the virtuous indignation of Doctor Goley, who is perpetually being summoned at indefensible moments to minister to the ailments of "Negus" or of "Puff."

Yes, Mrs. Chutney is great fun, cruelly vain, cruelly silly, but ready to join in anything that will afford amusement. She has got an awful liver, they say, and exists only on excitement, which is somewhat limited at "Our Station".

Our Colonel

The Commanding Officer of the Ninety-Eleventh, and of "Our Station," is Colonel Capsicum—a jolly, generous old fellow as ever donned the scarlet, or plunged a battalion into irreconcilable and irremediable position.

For twenty-seven years has old Capsicum been on civil employ at that out-of-the-way district Jehanumabad, and the blossoms of his early military career, now ripened into fruit, are exemplified by a happy obliviousness of everything connected with the military profession. The movements of a company might possibly be compassed by his attainments, acquired through the instrumentality of "dummies" on his dining-room table. But of battalion and brigade manœuvres, I suspect he knows about as much of them as the Grand Lama!

But these things grieve not old Capsicum. He smokes his meerschaum with none the less complacency for all the venial errors of an eccentric counter-march, and tells you his oft-repeated tale of some glorious exploit with a tiger when he was at Jehanumabad, with no thought soever of that very morning's exploit on the parade, when, by an inexplicable manœuvre and the hilarity of his charger, he was all but the victim of contiguous bayonets.

A capital old fellow is Capsicum! but his figure is not designed by nature for equestrian performances; a circumstance which militates against his efficiency and his personal security in the saddle, as may be fully illustrated by his movements thereon, which are about as eccentric as the occasional movements of his regiment. But as the temperature of Jehanumabad was more favourable to a lounge in a barouche than to such a heat-generating operation as equestrian exercise, his skill, however perfect originally, had ample opportunity to subside. Just drop in after your ride, at early breakfast, when you will find him in his verandah; take a cup of coffee with him (and you will pronounce it uncommonly good too, for he indoctrinates his slaves into the mysteries of culinary correctness), and you will hear all about Jehanumabad, and how he established never-ending canals for irrigation, and fathomless tanks for the supply of water to a parched population. How, through the mildness of his rule and the beneficence of his sway, he turned a waste into a smiling land, and raised the revenue from the imaginary to the tangible. And then, if I mistake not, you will be told of the sports of the field, and how tigers, elephants, and bears dropped spontaneously before his unerring rifle.

Communicative is "our Colonel," unquestionably; but only allude to the domestic arrangements, and your succeeding hours are irretrievably engaged. His soul in set unremittingly upon devices for the better government of his house as regards a reduction in the temperature and wonderful works of science and of art are projected and elaborated for this laudable object. His latest conception is a patent "Thermantidote"—what an English agriculturist would take to be a gigantic winnowing-machine. Your especial attention will be drawn to the original idea of having the cool air impelled into the room by a certain peculiar form of fan, which revolves, if I remember right, at the rate of a hundred and fifty thousand miles an hour or thereabouts! There, in that verandah, you see the slave grinding away at the wheel, which never ceases, day or night.

If you go inside the room, you will practically experience the effects by finding your hat blown off into an adjacent corner, and your hair blown indiscriminately and unpleasantly about your eyes and face! And as there is a corresponding thermantidote hurling its Boreas blasts from the opposite verandah, and a superpending punkah, which waves recklessly and defiantly above your head, you only need a current from the ground to be involved in a general hurricane-a perfect cyclone. So what with the tatties—those moistened furze screens that close up every other aperture—"Our Colonel" has unquestionably the coolest house at Kabob. And we have opportunities, many and oft, for appreciating it, as "Our Colonel" gives no end of dinner-parties; and the claret and beer submitted to the refrigerating influences of his ingenious devices are soothing and appeasable to the desiccated throats on a summer's eve.

There is the Colonel, as usual, in his verandah. His Adjutant has polished off the duties of his diurnal visit, which is effected at this early hour, and has taken his departure. Mrs. Capsicum, after her morning's drive, has vanished to the innermost recesses of her secret chamber, to court repose and sip tea after the terrific exertion. And for a time, until the heat is unpleasant, he will sit there, with elevated leg, indulging in his meerschaum, which has replaced the hookah, that pipe of other days. There his table attendant is giving him his coffee, whilst another menial fans the fire in that locomotive grate where the kettle boils, in due preparation for the wants of coming visitors, who drop in to "have a jaw" with the Colonel, and while away an hour in listening again to his oft-told tales, and imparting to him in return the real news of "Our Station."

Our Colonel's Wife

$\mathcal{I}$ just recommend you to exercise a judicious caution when you enter Mrs. Capsicum's drawing-room, if you have the slightest regard for your shins' epidermis. For, to encourage coolness, precautionary measures of a most rigid nature, as decreed by the Colonel, are set against the intrusion of light, and the venetians hermetically sealed,

"Close latticed to the brooding heat,"

admitting no hospitable ray, make it so dark that you need to be well on the alert to avoid fracturing your limbs or capsizing the Bohemian glass that is so profusely scattered about on the marble-topped tables.

Mrs. Capsicum, who rejoices in this dim obscure, is wife of Our Colonel, and I have shrewd suspicion that she is the absolute, if not the acknowledged, commandant of the gallant Blazers. Only venture on military matters, and you will be edified with a detailed narrative of all that is going on in "Our Regiment," from the number of sick in hospital, with all their maladies, to the wigging administered to young Kirrich that

identical morning on the Parade. Quite maternal, too, is Mrs.
Capsicum, patronizing the young officers of "Our Regiment"
to an unlimited extent, and delighting to give them a mother's
advice. Now, as counsel, when coupled with champagne, is
not to be rejected or despised, our boys, I must confess it,
accept her invitations and advice with a becoming cheerfulness,
that evinces no lack of wisdom. But Mrs. Capsicum has a
quiver full of her own. To hear her dilate upon the merits,
qualifications, and virtues of each, diversified with a
descriptive roll of their individual points of attraction, will be
a relish at your morning's call. Her eldest boy, you will not
fail to hear, is a cadet at college. He is so very clever, and of
course will carry off all the prizes, and come out as number
one at the very least. From this scion of the noble dynasty of
Capsicum down to the most recent addition to the family,
every secret will be divulged, and your especial attention will
be invited to the relative ages of Toony and Motee at the
period when they were respectively weaned; while a
chronological history of the shedding of every tooth, and the
circumstance of Lucretia, the baby, having cut a third tooth
last Sunday morning, will be duly impressed upon you.

A dashing dresser is Mrs. Capsicum; always revelling in
gorgeous array, to the enrichment of all the cloth-merchants
of Kabob. Chouse Loll, the great *Koprawallah*, is eternally at
her house. I see his big bundles blocking up her door every
day. Whatever you chance to need from that wealthy
merchant, of course he has just sold it all to Mrs. Capsicum.
Depend upon it, the old rascal is hanging about her verandah
at this very moment; and there is Mrs. Capsicum amidst her
Sanhedrim of tailors, who are perpetually plying the needle
in her behalf; for everything is manufactured in that sunny
verandah, from a baby's bib to a bonnet; and the tryings-on
are infinite.

But Mrs. Capsicum revels in the millinery department, and is a shining light in the Dorcas Society. She is perpetually elaborating articles of fancy-work for the grand fair which is held annually. Take my word for it, you'll be inveigled by her to contribute to swell the treasures of her stall, the slightest donation being gratefully received. On the last occasion, Captain Kulum, with generous zeal, made an offering of a cartoon, representing a hoop hanging upon a hat-peg, executed with consummate skill and an undeniable amount of finish. This realized of the current coin of the realm sixteen rupees (or one pound twelve shillings exactly). So you perceive that talent is duly appreciated at Kabob.

And I must say that the fair needlepliers of Kabob are wonderfully prolific. Hecatombs of worsted-work are generated with a degree of celerity only to be rivalled by the expertness of the performance. Bottle-covers, pincushions, doilies, rugs, and polkajackets are legion. But all these combined sink numerically into insignificance, overshadowed, as they invariably are, by the preponderating amount of babies' socks that come to light; the production of which in such exuberance warrants the supposition that the demand for such commodities at "Our Station" is coequal to the supply. And judging from the accumulation of infantry at the Band, coupled with the domestic occurrences that appear in the *Kabob Weekly Chronicle,* the supposition might find acceptable grounds for confirmation.

Nor is the millinery business at an end here; for Mrs. Capsicum patronizes the German Mission, and assists Mrs. Fruitz, the large wife of the little Missionary, in disposing of the fancy goods which are consigned to her care from Germany for the benefit of the mission. Great boxes, with the articles appraised and ticketed by the fair hands of Mrs.

Capsicum herself, are disseminated by her throughout the four quarters of cantonments.

Mrs. Capsicum participates with the Colonel in the good old Indian notions of hospitality, which they had but little opportunity of evidencing at Jehanumabad and so they make up for lost time, by frequently welcoming at their festive board the community of Kabob, both small and great. And delightful little parties they give, I assure you; not wholesale entertainments, when large batches of the community are "knocked over" at a single discharge, suggesting a feeling of business being effected, and the mob rapidly disposed, when the dishes are cold and the liquids hot; but quiet parties, limited in number of guests, and where the beer and the claret roll icily down the throat, and the conversation, under such influences, is cheerful and brisk.

Then the Capsicums ate in their glory! The gallant Colonel cracks his jokes with an extra gush of humour, while Mrs. Capsicum makes glad the fleeting hours, presiding at the piano, and instituting an extempore *deux temps,* or polka, for those who are addicted to the dance; for, even at Jehanumabad, where, save the village gong, no music

> "Its valleys and rocks ever heard,"

and amid the rearing of her domestic brood, she did not forsake her piano, which added materially to her own immediate comfort then, and augments now the happiness of the musicians of Kabob, who have enlisted her as a performer in the Great Harmonic Meetings which periodically occur.

The Capsicums, thus affording, as they do, a never-failing source of generous, open-hearted sociability, have not unnaturally acquired for themselves the good opinion and the good wishes of the residents at "Our Station."

Our Padre

Our Spiritual Pastor and Master at Kabob is the Rev. Josiah Ginger, unctuous in appearance, redolent of fat, and with a face beaming like the sun on a gravel-walk!

A worthy divine of the *Ancien Régime* is " Our Padre," as the pastors of our flocks are denominated throughout the East; his views are of the broad and popular kind, he looks upon it that pastimes and pleasures of this mundane sphere can be participated in by the Clergy without any invested longitude of visage or sanctimoniousness of gait. He cannot discover that holiness must be exhibited by a concomitant exhibition of the whites of one's eyes; that purity of life is necessarily expressed by a white neck-tie, or practical piety by a rigidity of limb. He considers that the duties of the pastor may well be enlivened by the sports of the field; and that creeds and confectionery, doctrines and devilled kidneys, spirituality and sociability, may consistently run hand in hand, while hams and hermetically-sealed delicacies are not entirely irreconcilable with heavenly-mindedness. And we must confess it, that the combinations are effected with

striking and satisfactory results, as we find that the salad of
the Saturday, as manufactured by "Our Padre" at mess, in no
way clashes with the sermon of the Sunday. The sick in
hospital are visited and attended zealously and lovingly,
though he does drive a dog-cart, patronize the Sky races, and
burn the midnight oil over a pool at billiards or at a rubber of
whist.

Mrs. Ginger is in England, looking after a domestic flock
of little Gingers, since which time Ginger has become a
member of our mess, to the manifest improvement in the
cookery. The concoction of savoury stews, and the
ministration of devilled toast on improved principles, have
been instituted and established by him with unqualified
applause.

To be sure, we do hear it affirmed that "Our Padre" is a
little too precipitate in his movements from church, and that
his exit from pulpit, disrobing, and departure from their
genuflexions, and that he "polishes off" the service, as it is
heathenly expressed, in a manner that suggests hot coffee
waiting at the mess.

Then we have allusions, but decidedly of a less objective
nature, upon the brevity of the discourses. Certainly Ginger,
in his delivery, does not hang fire. He disengages himself of
his sentiments with an *aplomb* signally attractive, and which
keeps the soldiery awake; for to be borne away from one's
couch at the least suffocating hour of the early morning; and
then to be deposited under the soporific influence of a punkah,
exposed to the drowsy drawlings of a parson who attenuates
his words to the fullest limit of his breath, is apt indeed to
restore one to the land of Nod!

Now, Ginger, we must confess it, doesn't give his
congregation a chance. He tells his tale with telling brevity
and unction. And what though scandal does declare that he

possesses a series of sermons which are gone through in rotation with as rigid a regularity as the movements of the planetary bodies! What of that? A good thing can't be told too often; and if the matter is pronounced to be of a mild texture, Ginger can, when he likes, preach "tellingly," and touch the hearts of his hearers, I can assure you, as on the occurrence of a recent fatal catastrophe at Kabob, the sermon delivered on the occasion, and which was obviously original, set off some of the "weaker vessels" into explosive sobs, accompanied with hysteria, whilst the main body of the congregation went boo-hooing out of church.

So close to the sacred pile, let us step on and explore its architectural beauties. That sable janitor, who holds the living at the gate, will unfold its pea-green portals. His functions are to protect the sacred edifice from spoliation and wrong. The duties of this other venerable Oriental consist in preparing

"The taper's glimmering light"

for the evening service, and furnishing fire for—"Our Padre's" cheroot.

This, then, is the steeple but "the soft, sweet chimes of the Sabbath bells, that so peacefully float from afar!" peal only in the lively imagination. The calling to prayers at Kabob is effected by a less elaborate process: a heathen, " simple and unadorned," scales recklessly the lofty walls, through the instrumentality of an infirm ladder, and then and there bangs spasmodically and intermittently on a discordant gong, until "Our Padre" is attired in his vestments, when the lamplighter, with preconcerted views, rushes frantically forth, and shouts "No more, no more." Mark the interior economy of the structure: that timber receptacle, which does double duty— not of "a bed by night, a chest of drawers by day," but of pulpit as well as of reading-desk—those communion-rails, that table now bereft of its cover, that font. Observe the purity of the ecclesiastical style of architecture selected, obviously the early Indian or Carpenteresque, one of the periods of the "Disappointed Gothic."

But there goes Ginger; that is his bungalow into which you see he has just driven, and all that multitude of "the sick, the maimed, the lame, the halt, and the blind," that are thronging in at his gate are the afflicted ones of Kabob, and of the surrounding villages, who come in for the food which is distributed to them weekly from the Compassionate Fund, which Ginger established, and of which he is almoner. Did you ever set eyes on such a mass of infirmity, decrepitude, and human disorganization? There is a genuine leper; and there you may see a real, living picture of those crowds of impotent folk who thronged the highways of Judæa some eighteen centuries ago, and who waited expectantly by Bethesda's pool for an anticipated cure.

Come in and see Ginger. He will give you a hearty welcome and some excellent bitter beer. His sanctum will recall your college days—gowns, guns, and hunting-whips promiscuously combine: here a MS. sermon lies complacently by a cookery-book and a *Bell's Life*, while there a packet of letters and a prospectus of the Sky races, with the hospital report and a receipt for milk-punch.

But Ginger is engaged. I find a poor gunner died this morning, and he is off to bury him.

Thus, you see, with the sick and afflicted thronging at his gate, and the dead awaiting interment, "Our Padre," amid the flash of light and cheerful pleasures, has many a sterner duty to perform, from which he never flinches; and if he participates in the sports and amusements of the gay and the healthy, he can and does share in the sorrows of the bereaved, sympathize with the afflicted, and cheer the couch of the sick. Ask the soldiers in the barracks, they are the best judges. But you need not go so far, for the fact is well recognized at "Our Sation."

OUR PADRE

Page No. 28

OUR JOINT MAGISTRATE

Page No. 33

OUR MALL Page No. 3

OUR MISSIONARY Page No. 4

Our Joint Magistrate and Collector

Huldey is the man—an incipient lawgiver and judge. He has just passed through the probation of an Assistant; and with accumulated powers for the punishment of wickedness and vice and the adjudication of minor cases, he has now been promoted to assist our Magistrate, and so rejoices in the associative designation of "Joint."

In the social circle Huldey is very grand. He is a bit of a dandy, curls his hair, cherishes the rudiments of a moustache, and nourishes oleaginously the sprouts of an early whisker. Being sportingly inclined, he possesses a stud of horses, and cultivates dogs, rakish in cut and hairy in pretensions. At daybreak every morning is Huldey to be seen at the race-course, disguised in top-boots and coat of an amazing cut, training his Arab. The Sky races are to take place shortly, and Huldey and Godower the sporting Ensign are great promoters of the meeting. They have established a confederacy, and are very dark in their proceedings. Then Huldey rattles off across the fields, to give the dogs a little exercise, and canters home leisurely as the sun begins to wax warm.

He lives in that bungalow near the Cutcherry, where you'll find him soon: his sporting habiliments are discarded; the shirt-sleeves of comfort, the slippers of ease, together with the flowing draperies of coolness, usurp the place of boots and leather inexpressibles, the jockey cap yields to the more genial Glengarry; and so our friend, seated in his verandah, holds his morning court. He is supposed to listen to the daily reports, to hear complaints, and perform official business at this early hour. Of course he is most attentive; the Gazette in his hand, with an account of the Gronepore races is merely a toy; while the sable officials, reading away for the very life, utterly regardless of stops, monotonously and nasally race over the documents, swinging their shawled bodies backwards and forwards. Huldey hears all about it, but he does not overlook how that Phizgig with 10 stone has beaten Screwdriver carrying 8 stone 4 lb. Then he lights his cheroot and sips his tea, which, with a slice of buttered toast, his table attendant has brought and placed alongside of him, while his favourite dog Forceps, something between pariah and a buggy-rug, sits by expectantly. Thus public and domestic matters progress congenially.

By-and-by, cased in a suit of flannel, "Our Joint" goes forth, and in that attire perhaps drops in and pays some lady a morning visit on his way to Court. Then, if you come across him, and draw him out in the magisterial line, you will ascertain confidentially, that in his private opinion he considers the Judge an awful ass, and a perfect ignoramus in point of law (between ourselves, Turmeric has reversed nearly all his decisions); and great is his grievance at the latest reversal, for most unquestionably was he justified in sentencing the prisoner, a domestic servant, to three years' hard labour on the roads for purloining his master's water-pot. Like Turmeric, he instantly refers to Act 21 of 17, and Regulation 6 of 94, which thoroughly and conclusively establish his view of the question. Then, as for Chutney, his immediate superior, he considers him to be a downright gaby of the first water, and only fit to count the heads of the prisoners in the jail.

In the evening we shall again see him, driving to the band in his curricle; and later still we may meet him, extensively got up in sables and white cravat, scented profusely with some potent essence, telling the ladies of his Arab's exploit, and how he can do his half-mile in fifty-one seconds, and what he himself did that morning at office in the case of Tinkerdoss *versus* Beer Loll, and how the Omlah of the Court (who, I am told, is a functionary of the most consummate importance) congratulated him on the wisdom of his adjudication; all of which interesting communication impresses his fair hearers with the idea, that without him the district in particular, as well as India in general, would go to everlasting smash. But "Our Joint" is a valuable acquisition; his modest self-appreciation always renders him a willing associate, ready to join in whatever will promote sociality, conviviality, and the like. Indispensable is he to the Thespians. His willingness to undertake the mildest characters, such as Hamlet and Macbeth, evince the latent spark of theatrical genius that smoulders within him, which can only find vent in sickly melodrama or derogatory farce. Nothing comes amiss to "Our Joint" when our parson is absent, the prayers of the devout Church are read by him. I verily believe he would with equal willingness with the Pope and all his Cardinals, or, with equal promptitude and despatch, prepare a work for the press on heresy and schism, heavy gun drill, and the plurality of worlds. Thus, with such rare talent, are we not fortunate in having so desirable an acquisition at "Our Station?"

Our Mall

Of course you will take a drive on the Mall, to "eat the air," as we call it in Eastern phraseology. Eat the air? Yes, and a grateful refreshment indeed, after being cribbed, cabined, and confined within the precincts of your closed bungalow for the many and the dreary hours of an Indian summer day—hours which "immeasurably spread, seem lengthening as they go." Glad, indeed, to be able to venture forth from your house of bondage, released from a captivity enforced by the bars and getters of a scorching sun and the blasts of a fiery furnace!

Oh, for the joys of an Indian summer day! "Angels and ministers of grace defend us!" A summer day, indeed! when the bright green meadows "are daisied o'er with lambs," and the gay earth, with verdure clad, gladdens the eyesight as it ranges "o'er the blue hills and far away, beyond their utmost purple rim" with a balmy air,

"Distill'd with the fragrance of flowers,
When the sunbeams bespangle the dew-emm'd fields,

And the birds carol loud in the bowers."

And all that sort of thing?

Not exactly! See the lovely Kabob enveloped in burning sand; observe " the mighty pathos of its empty streets," save when some insane native is to be seen, enshrouded in the folds of his toga, buffeting the blast and daring the sun's rays, which threaten to singe him to destruction. Or when some more culpably insane lover of England's blood, rushes frantically forth to court the object of his admiration (in which case I detect a signal display of undisguised affection worthy of success). Go you forth and face the fierce fury of the elements on this bright Indian summer day, if anything is seductive enough to tempt you from the comparative coolness of a well-regulated punkah—go you and experience the withering effects of the simoom, which curdles your very marrow, and say if anything can again draw you from your lair while the angry sun shines still, and until the fury of wind has abated. And let me honestly confess it, the wind does blow right savagely at Kabob with forty fiery furnace power. Be immured, then, in your bungalow from sunrise (and a precious early riser is the sun) to sunset, and you will appreciate a drive in the comparative coolness of the evening.

Let us away, then, to the Mall, where the beauty and fashion are to be seen, though but for a few brief moments, as so "sudden droppeth down the night," the brightness of fair ones' eyes is exchanged for the brightness of buggy-lamps which are called into requisition.

This, then, is the Mall, which, you perceive, enjoys the exclusive felicity of having its Sahara-like surface watered, to the manifest advantage of the ladies' bonnets, which, until reform was effected, universally exhibited a uniform drab, Pawney of ours, whose wife has an annual consignment of a

French bonnet direct from her *modiste,* the arrival and display of which is one of the events of the season, and affords pabulum for conversation at Kabob for a good fortnight; and whose latest importation (that orange concoction, with fiery, flaming feather) being totally and irretrievably ruined on the very first night of its public exhibition—Mrs. Pawney's husband, I say, couldn't stand it any longer, so, by superhuman exertion and pungent appeals to the pockets of the community, eleemosynary donations were got in, and orders on the Paymaster for monthly deductions for this laudable object were obtained, and the watering of the Mall was a *fait accompli*— an achievement which operates most effectually towards the social gathering together of our little society. And we do it in a primitive way, as the patriarchs of old had the ground watered in front of their tents—not with jets shot from those abominations of wheeled carts, objects of terror to incipient Jehus and shying horses, but the simple, unadulterated fluid sprinkled from the protruding palm of the "drawer of water."

The Mall is not so well attended to-night, for there is a grand feed at the Chutneys's, and Mrs. Teapoy of ours is to have a hop, so that the ladies who are going to each place are lying by.

There goes Topey and his wife in their buggy. Topey is commissariat officer, popularly designated "Grambags." He furnishes the soldiery with "beer, wine, tobacco, sugar, pepper, and snuff," and other varieties too numerous to mention. A capital fellow is "Grambags," and his wife is a stunner. That woman in the white habit is Mrs. Byle, wife of that artillery officer who is riding with her. He commands the Cow Battery—called so, because the guns are drawn by the horned species. A capital rider is Mrs. Byle, and a dead hand at the polka. Those were her children we met just now on ponies, with a bevy of attendants. Those in the dog-cart are some of

"Ours." But as the Mall is cleared, and the *"bheesties"* alone are left to hold their undisputed sway, let us be off to the Band, where we shall be sure to see something more of the live portion of "Our Station."

Our German Missionary

Down in the principal bazaar, at the very west end of Kabob, which, although the least fashionable, is the most highly peopled quarter of "Our Station," in that whitewashed bungalow which stares conspicuously amidst its mud-coloured neighbours, like a white-robed native in a crowd of his unvestured brethren, resides the Reverend Emanuel Fruitz, the little German Missionary, his family (a perfect colony in itself, and, therefore, not to be disregarded in this faithful record), and the converts to his faith, whose members might be comprised within a not over-extensive range of apartments.

If the Reverend Emanuel Fruitz is himself diminutive in stature (and why the German Missionaries are invariable little men has not been satisfactorily accounted for), his zeal is fully an equivalent, and his moral worth amply compensates for the lack of muscular development. Besides, as already insinuated, his progeny are, at any rate numerically, if not physically, large; whilst of the sharer of his earthly joys there is no denying it, that she is of a stately and enormous size, completely overshadowing the little Fruitz when, sitting together in their well-stocked four-wheeler, they take their evening drive. And, by the way, a most surprising vehicle that is. The accommodation it affords, the *multum in parvo* nature of its capabilities, are only to be equalled by the tenacity of its wheels, which, while wabbling so unmercifully, suggestive of immediate disorganization, yet remain steadfastly faithful amidst all their revolutions. While in the horse I recognize, in his moral character, an emblem of the little Missionary himself—patient, enduring, and meek. He has a duty to perform, and he puts his shoulder to the collar with a hearty will, although the load is great, the roads heavy, and the progress slow. A proper Missionary's horse is that!

A perfect Salamander is the little Fruitz. He defies the rigour of the scorching wind, and at any hour of the day you may find him in the highways and byways holding forth to the native community on the subject of his mission—scattering the seeds, as he will tell you. And this simple duty, it appears, he is well satisfied to perform, without the satisfaction of reaping the fruits thereof, for at Kabob the heathen resoluel to accede to his views of entertaining a novel faith, and resist the logic of his reasonings. Sheltered under the canopy of his wide-spreading mushroom, he enforces his doctrines in all weathers. There he is, discussing a point with two of the natives, while casual passers-by pause awhile to hear the debate, and little urchins drop their screechings and their games to listen to the proceedings.

Fruitz has established a school in the Bazaar, which I am told, is populously attended. And Mrs. Fruitz takes under her protecting wing the little orphans that Fruitz in his labours carries home to cherish and bring up. Those were the orphans you saw in the Fruitz's verandah, and it was for the nourishment of those same ones that the proceeds of the last fancy sale in the cantonment were devoted, and for whom little Fruitz pleaded in broken English, with convulsive gestures, in Ginger's pulpit a few Sundays ago.

A very excellent little fellow is Fruitz, but it is to be hoped that his orations in the Oriental vernacular are couched in language more intelligible to his hearers than are his efforts in English. But his sermon, which was all about a "winny-ya-ard," was an affecting one, albeit the solemnity of the discourse was endagered by the eccentricity of the English, which, I must confess, excited the cachinnations of several members of our otherwise discreet congregation.

Hawnster of ours, who was so irreverent as to evince merriment, pleaded in extenuation that the conversion by the little missionary of a "Jewish Rabbi" into a "Jewish Wabbi" justified a temporary explosion of mirth. But Fruitz accompanies his eloquence with manual exercises of a theatrical order, waving his arms, and, with his little body reposing on the pulpit-cushion, describes in the air, as though he were floating on the sea and buffeting a huge crimson billow.

Then Fruitz has a rival in the Roman Catholic priest, and great are the contentions between the zealous missionaries. As the latter is a Maltese, and can only speak bad Italian, broken French, a smattering of Hindustani, and dislocated English, how the disputants convey their respective sentiments to each other is a problem the solution of which has not transpired. But the contentions wax warm at times, and rumours are floated to the "Lines" that some convert, seduced and clandestinely appropriated from the rival fold, has excited an agitation not entirely confined to words. We did hear that one convert had been induced to change his creed for the superior monthly stipend that would fall to his lot when in the rival fold, and so he became a Roman Catholic, that a subsequent raising of the emoluments by his original pastor at once restored him to Protestantism, and that the allurement of a higher grade of pay reconverted him instantly to the Papal belief. When, once more, by an enhancement of the Protestant premium, he was only too willing to abjure the Pope and again throw himself into the congregation of the little Fruitz. Be this as it may, the much-vexed question, it is further reported, was submitted to arbitration, when the object of dispute, on the intimation that pecuniary aid would be reduced and equalized in either creed, scornfully rejected the offer, and went down forthwith to the great hideous idol in the Temple of Kabob and proclaimed himself to be an unadulterated Hindoo.

But the little Fruitz perseveres right manfully, and in the faithful Mrs. Fruitz he has a very able coadjutor.

Go and see the Mission House. You will find Mrs. Fruitz, who, with smiles and much broken English, will be delighted to show you the establishment where the orphans are educated, with a view to their being able to reap for themselves an honest livelihood.

And so, amidst toil and travail, and disappointment, with contracted means, exiled in a foreign land, but with hopes bright and a firm faith, do this good, worthy couple minister, individually and conjointly, in what is to them a labour of love, working with willing hearts in the arduous duties of that state of life to which they have been called, to the benefit of their fellow-creatures and the cordial good wishes of the society of "Our Station."

Our Doctor

Dr. Goley is Civil Surgeon, and lives in the Civil Lines. The soldiers of the artillery and the staff are exposed to the influence of Doctor De Why; while Dr. McGhee is the consulting physician and general practitioner of "Ours" and all three repose beneath the superintending and vigilant glance of the great Dr. Fogrum, whose responsible and arduous duties consist in permanently sitting as president of a standing committee to provide for the sick and needy in their affliction, by the administering of medical certificates, which enable the then joyful recipients to escape for a while from their exile in the shadeless plains of Ind, to

"Breathe in luxury their native air."

Dr. McGhee, it might be unmistakably affirmed, from his uncompromising accent, originated and had his early development matured in the Land of Cakes. In general aspect, his physiognomy is characteristic of severity: the impending brows, which project like cornices, cast a deep shade upon those cold grey eyes, that seem to shrink appalled with instinctive horror at the too dangerous proximity of that fiery nose.

In creed, McGhee is a Christian; in character he is Hebraic, being of an acquisitive and accumulative turn of mind, which resolves itself into performances that afford food for the amusement of the young blood of Kabob and the enlivenment of the coffee-shop.

The domestic hearth of "Our Doctor" is cheered with a better half, who is the sharer of his joys and the participator in his profits. He has stamped his similitude upon a buxom lassie, who, brought up and nourished in her fond father's homestead, rejoices in a limited amount of knowledge, a powerful resemblance to the maternal parent, and the name of Barbara.

But what the internal economy of the McGhee household exhibits, has never been made visible to the naked eye of our community. The seclusion of a China and a Japan has nought to compare with the rigid interdiction of all intercourse from without, that signalizes the government of the McGhee rule, in respect to the non-admission of the foreigner; for hermetically sealed are the garden gates, and the glad voice of welcome rings not within its walls. Is it lest the pledge of their earliest affections, in the form of the gentle Barbara, might be reft from the domestic bosom by some susceptible stripling, convulsed into enamourment, and entrapping her in the meshes of matrimony? Or is it that morning visits engender evening spreads, and that buggies at the door are provocative of bitter beer at the table—concatenations which involve pecuniary consequences of a serious nature?

The paternal McGhee has a penetrating eye for the main chance. The duties of his profession-the medicinal and the surgical—no longer molest that brain, from which any acquirements he may have realized on the subject in his early days have long since exuded. The popular impression is, that he is a veritable "Revolver," while the ladies look upon him as a prefect "Herod" among their children. Such being the views entertained, the really sick ones of "Ours" are never submitted to his destructive powers; and so the leisure of the "Great Plague of Kabob" is occupied in a more genial way, by devotion of the business of the Kabob Bank.

Of course you have heard of the Kabob Bank! Well, it was originated and established by McGhee, who is the very life and soul of it. He is a director; so is Stickerdoss, the nigger; so are Ensign Loan, and Neel, the indigo-planter; and so is Pysa Doss, the contractor. These are the bank parlour authorities. Scraps is secretary. Scraps came to India as a recruit, and being originally a tailor, got a snip to purchase his discharge: then he became a river merchant, diffusing all the trash of the metropolis along the banks of the great Gunga. Now he is shareholder, manager, and secretary of the great Kabob Bank. He will transact any amount of business with you in that bank parlour, but always under the secret ministration of old McGhee. Just drop in and ask for the loan of a lakh. You will be delighted with the fluency with which the great man will dilate upon shares, floating deposits, securities, liquidations, remittances, exchange, insurance, mortgage, premiums, policies, government paper, and the like.

Between you and me, it is said, and Goley affirms it to be so,—but, from his having been profusely bled by the Bank, his opinion might be somewhat biased, and his mind prejudiced,—but still it is said that old McGhee does funny things in that quiet bank parlour-cancelling shares in a peculiarly acquisitive, and not altogether unprofitable manner, and performing other delicate but lucrative operations, which augment and develop the resources of his individual purse.

But the mighty maw of McGhee is not appeased with such mild nourishment, and craves nutrition from other sources; so that he established the *Kabob Chronicle,* of which he is sole proprietor. He is a great shareholder in the "General Nullah Navigation Company," as also in the "More Effectual Nigger-Clothing Company," and others too numerous to mention.

But, here he comes in his buggy, with his horsekeeper seated beside him. That buggy, built some fifty years ago, is still tenacious of existence; but, like the human frame, is ever in a state of active renovation. The horse, too, is, worthy of your regard. It was a cavalry charger, cast from the ranks for unsoundness, general debility, and old age, and was purchased by McGhee at auction for eightpence halfpenny. And just see how the blood of the once proud Arabian tells; he will work while he has a spark of life left in him. And he certainly does not lead an idle life with old McGhee, whom he is now drawing to visit his hospital, which, taking into consideration the sport that he finds there morning and evening, bears the impressive designation "Our Doctor's Preserves."

"Good evening, Doctor. Warm evening—eh?" There he goes; he doesn't hear. His thoughts are too much occupied with rupees, and with what he can best do to turn a penny out of some one at "Our Station."

OUR DOCTOR Page No. 45

OUR DOCTOR'S WIFE Page No. 49

OUR INVALID'S FAMILY

Page No. 5

OUR SPINS

Page No. 5

Our Doctor's Wife

In that small dingy bungalow, with its thatch all dishevelled and deranged, its pillars pealed of their whitewash, and verging hopelessly from the perpendicular. Its once green venetians bereft of their hinges, hanging about with similar obliquity of purpose, and yet evincing a determination to blockade the doors. The compound bared of every symptom of vegetation, and denuded of all human life. There, in that demesne, and staring at you like a bleared and dismal waste, a howling wilderness, where the jackals at their midnight orgies love to roam, and give vent to their lamentations in wails, long, lachrymose, and loud,—where the crowd of vagrant dogs, too, from the contiguous Bazar, restort to bay the moon, and serenade the inmates,—is there domesticated with her lord the spouse of our far-famed Doctor; there is domiciled the gentle Barbara; and there are ripening to maturity the small blossoms that are designed to perpetuate the dynastic brood of the McGhees.

The interior of that family mansion, as already recorded, is not generally exposed to public view. But still, the inner life of the McGhees is not altogether unknown to fame, for the secrets of the prison-house are divulged with a degree of circumstantial evidence that justifies occasional belief. Now, we all know, for instance, and we heard it through Mrs. Brisket's ayah (one of those Oriental creatures of the genus lady's-maid), who had been in Mrs. McGhee's service, who told Mrs. Nutkut's ayah, who whispered it to Mrs. Garlic, who mentioned it to Garlic, who repeated it at mess, that Mrs. McGhee often whops Barbara because she doesn't get married. But ayahs are shockingly given to embroidery, and are as spiteful as loquacious and we cannot repose trust in all they assert, or we might also credit that unscrupulous rumour, also promulgated through the ayahistic agency, to the effect that old Mother McGhee, who is mightily cannie in the things that are visible, is still more deplorably so in the things not seen, and that, as the ayah herself expressed it, she never did come across such a "Mem Sahib"—that her wardrobe which is visible to the naked eye, is a mere japan or veneer, and that her invisible garments are about as scanty as the skirts of a Highlander. And though it is confirmed by Mrs. Jootmoot, the demi-semi Oriental who lives in the Bazar, and dispenses cheap second hand millinery to the soldiers' wives, and whom Mrs. McGhee once delighted to honour, yet Mrs. Jootmoot is horribly prejudiced. For Mrs. McGhee has withdrawn her custom, because she had the audacity to bring up old McGhee at the last "Court of Requests," for refusing to pay her little bill of long standing, and who had, *vulgo*, to stump up; a decree much to the mortification of the matron, and the gratification of the subs of "Ours" who were members of the Court, and who are frequently entertained by the settlement of such petty pecuniary disaccordances.

Chouse Lall, the great cloth merchant, considers it a profitless operation to have dealings with Mrs. McGhee.

Being an influential personage, he resists the missives that are sent to allure him into her presence. But Mrs. McGhee is triumphant over the petty *boxwallahs*, those itinerant purveyors of lucifer-matches, ginger, salmon, castor oil, shaving-soap, pickles, note paper, and bridles. She despatches her emissaries (the Doctor's orderlies, who are enlisted, *vi et armis*, in her service), and the recreant pedlars are haled into her presence, to their unmitigated disgust, to the general ransacking of their boxes, an abstraction, at nominal prices, of their choicest treasures, with hopes faint and undefined of pecuniary compensation.

There comes Mrs. McGhee, in her trap, drawn by one of those gargling, groaning, gaunt "ships of the desert"—being preferred to horses by the cannie Doctor, as being less addicted to gram. And, really, a capital camel it is!—drags that palankeen carriage at a good ten miles an hour. Though it is a caution to the passing traveller, I am not quite satisfied whether the terror inspired on the minds of horses when it passes, arises from the awkward gait and general uncouthliness of the animal, or from the uproarious clamour of the vehicle itself, which rolls along with the spokes and tire of its wheels in a state of such loose dependancy as to stir up the noise of ten thousand anvils, sufficient to rouse the dead.

Though the domestic doors are shut, and her mansion inaccessible, the band plays to-night, and Mrs. McGhee then takes the opportunity of displaying her loved Barbara, for the special benefit of anyone intent on matrimony. And, by the way, they do say—but it must be apocryphal—that once some hapless wight, a needy sub involved in difficulties, and dunned by his creditors, conscious of the monetary value of old McGhee, did actually institute proposals for entering into the McGhee family. Under the combined influence of a champagne tiffin and an unanticipated advent of an obtrusive bailiff, rushed over to old McGhee, and inquired what he would "fork out" to get rid of his Barbara, whom the Griff in question then and there offered to take off his hands for a suitable indemnification. The report, as further particularized, records that the sum demanded was of so heavy a nature that the terms of the treaty were summarily rejected, and the bold Griff, with champagne subsided, and a bailiff departed, had cause to rejoice at old McGhee's declining his offer. But, to return from our digression: just go alongside Mrs. McGhee's carriage, and you will find her conversation delightful. If she knows little of the world beyond her compound gate, she can and will tell you narratives of herself: how that she "enjoys very bad health"—with a microscopic detail of her ailments, together with the treatment she has experienced, when the last poultice was applied and where, what the specific pains are that she endures, and what medicines did for her. But she is never so happy as when she becomes discursive upon the subject of dental surgery, from which you will, ascertain how and why she has been a martyr, with a thrilling circumstantiality which will, probably, have the effect of removing you from the carriage, bearing away in your mind the impression that the McGhees are decidedly, and palpably, a family that does not do over-much honour to "Our Station."

Our Invalid Major

As we are at his gate, we'll just step in and see Major Garlic. Unlucky in promotion, disgusted with incessantly tramping the parade-ground to little purpose, and no symptoms of a Staff appointment displaying themselves, even in the far-off horizon of his hopes, he made capital out of his constitution, cultivated a disordered state of liver, and got invalided.

In his early career, Garlic was a gay Lothario, delighting to bask in the sunshine of some loved one's smiles, and striving to captivate some blushing maid to bear the loving name of wife. He sought a bride. Although the multiplicity of his applications and entreaties to the maidens of Juwabpore, where he was stationed, won for him the soubriquet of the "Solicitor-General,' they were, one and all, impervious, unpropitious, unkind.

In terrible disgust, and with desperate resolve to announce with crushing effect his utter scorn for England's heartless daughters, he rushed simultaneously into folly and wedlock, and married a "darkie"—a pure and unmitigated specimen of the mild Hindoo; one of those dusky daughters of the East that roll their black effulgent orbs

"On India's coral strand."

Garlic is a sensible fellow now, and acknowledges that he played the part of a pretty considerable idiot. But his antipathy for the female sex has not diminished, nor has its violence abated. For, with a cunning eye and a keen relish, he diligently courts the weaknesses of frail women, and diffuses with immoderate glee, the petty peccadilloes of Eve's fair daughters, as, ever and anon, they reach his ear to tremble on his tongue.

Garlic has affected the census in a very material degree, having established a family on a scale of unlimited prodigality. His quiver is well stocked with a miscellaneous supply of every tincture and of every tinge. There is the unqualified coffee-colour, in its normal hue, with all the delicate varieties and gradations consequent upon the introduction of milk: there is the genuine, undeniable mud, the yellow, the tawny, and the pink. See, there are some of the olive-branches taking an airing in their trap. They bear the felicitous cognomen of "Garlic's Irregulars," and the vehicle itself revels in the appellation of "Garlic's Colour-box." Does not envy rankle in your breast at witnessing the happy lot of the parent invalid, at being the possessor of such a piebald progeny, with their tawny complexions, black eyes, and still blacker locks?

Dame Garlic is not patent to the vulgar world. Her habitations are in the dim obscure. She dwells, as it is orientally expressed, "behind the purdah." But in compliance with your entreaties, she may be induced at times to emerge and increase your satisfaction by displaying in your presence the zest with which she smokes her hookah, and chews her beetal-leaf. The once lithe, sylph-like, airy houri has merged through the inspiration of unlimited butter, into an obese, ring-nosed, unctuous matron.

Have a caution as you enter the house—that land of darkness. The floor is infested with the brats that lie dormant in every direction, with vestments of an abridged, if not of an entirely abrogated nature. The fumes of tobacco, commingled with the scent of the flavouring-essences, together with the pungent odour of Eastern confections and condiments undergoing the ordeal of concoction in the inner chambers, impregnate the air, which, unagitated by the grateful motion of a punkah, is stifling and oppressive; but Garlic is used to it, and the sable spouse and her tribe thrive spontaneously in this hotbed.

An amusing, clever fellow is Garlic: fond of his books, which to him are a source of domestic enjoyment—as well they may—and still more, desperately fond of an argumentative encounter; and is prepared, at the earliest opportunity, to dispute, expound, convince, and enforce his views on any possible, subject, against any comer, however formidable, and however acute. Get him on his *chabootra*—that terrace of masonry before his house, where he loves to sit when the shades of eve have "cooled the burning sky,"—and have a gentle chat with him. A pleasant hour it is for the Indian exile, when the easiest chairs that the bungalow can produce are brought forth, with supplementary ones for the especial consolation of the upraised legs; when the grateful cheroot, and still more grateful "peg"—that artful and insinuating compilation of soda-water and of brandy—are then instituted by the Pagan Ganymede; and the surrounding air is agitated by the large fan in the hand of a corresponding slave.

Then, as the stars begin to twinkle in the sky, through the canopy of blazing dust that is gradually dissolving, when the bats begin to signalize their existence by gyrations of rather too proximate a character to be pleasant, and when the Bazar has dropped its din, and before prowling jackals have commenced their midnight avocations or instituted their vocal inquietudes, then is the time for peace and enjoyment. Then you can pass a pleasant hour with the argumentative Garlic; when his black hive has ceased its buzz, when the sable matron has dropped her hubble-bubble, and retired to rest, and the black offspring are stretched on the floor of repose; then you can indulge in pipes and politics, discuss the merits of "pegs" and primogeniture, whilst the ballot and brandy-pawney play gratefully on the tongue, and retiring-pensions and military regulations combine pleasantly with the puffs of the punkah and the drafts of iced sodawater.

Then you will hear all Garlic's griefs, and his prospects for the future, which is irrevocably set in this far-off land. He once had bright hopes of a rest for his declining day, if not in the land of his birth, at any rate in the New World of Australia. But such visions have departed with the multiplication of the species, which yearly renders such dreams still more illusive!

No; Garlic has taken a step which he acknowledges will bind him irretrievably to the land of exile. Here he has made it his abiding-place, and here will he remain till he finds a still narrower home in the burial-ground of "Our Station."

Our Spins

*L*oveliness! that characteristic of British women, is but faintly exemplified among those at "Our Station," who recreate in the appellation of "Spins."

Barbara McGhee is a Spin; but in the popular eye she is regarded as impracticable. We discern in the bud what she will be in the flower. Safely may we predicate that she will eventually resemble her mamma in human architecture.

The bachelor mind, on matrimonial thoughts intent, pictures to itself the object of adoration as ever remaining the same delicate, pretty being that she now is. But to have such a dip into futurity, as is demonstrated by Barbara's mamma, especially as silly Mrs. McGhee persists in affirming that she was once exactly like Barbara, is a prospect quite sufficient to whirl away every project of a holy alliance. Moreover, who could possibly encounter the appalling prospect of having Mrs. McGhee plunging into the retirement of one's domestic hearth.

Next on our roster is Letitia Goley, sister to our civil surgeon, rather antique, but cleverish; a child of sentiment, the victim of tender sensibilities, and with a nose suggestive of a cricket-ball! Nine-and-twenty are the summers she has seen. With a few thousand rupees of her own, and a temper to match, she is decidedly eligible. She calls herself a brunette, and prides herself on her Spanish descent, which is about true, considering that Grandmamma Goley was indigenous, and powerfully tinctured with the blood of a Hindoo. It is currently reported that to "claim her hand unnumbered suitors came," but that she prefers the state of single-blessedness. She views matrimony in a sentimental light, and imagines that when love becomes a duty it must cease to be interesting; that wedlock would instantly blast the tendrils of affection, and sound a knell to expiring joy. We admire her doctrine, and allow her to remain single!

But Letitia is fond of society, and of small talk; goes to every party, and wears mittens. We have registered a small vow to eschew all partners (either temporarily in the dance, or for life) who wear mits. Damp digits are far from indispensable qualifications in a wife, and moist knuckles are anything but conducive to the heart's affections. But Letty is highly accomplished; she is a poet, perpetrates sonnets, which Herr Guttler, the band-master, sets to music. Her most brilliant composition was a heart-rending duet, commencing,

> "What are those vile knaves saying,
> Sinner, the whole day long?"

Then she warbles, too: sings a duet with Mrs. Chutney, all about a bank whereon something grows; but whether in time, or what time has to do with it, beyond that it is very wild, is exceedingly dubious. Then somebody dances with delight, and wonderful is the quivering and quavering at the word 'dances.' However, the novelty of the song is charming.

Next, we have Bella Clove, with plenty of head, and a scarcity of brain; a great adept at slang, and all goggle and gums. Rising sixteen, she has the skittishness of a two-year-old, and will soon entangle some amorous ensign by her rolick and rattle, backed up as it is with those bright hazel eyes, that twinkle so attractively, and that merry laugh. Bella is daughter of Clove of ours, who imported her last cold weather. Very little does she trouble her papa in the chaperoning line. For Bella scorns attendance. She rattles all about cantonment on that little Arab of hers; scampers round the racecourse in the morning with the young ensigns; gallops at full speed down the Mall with a similar escort, to the intense horror of poor Mrs. Dhurrter, who drives out in her buggy by herself, and whose horse, startled by the rushing tramp of hoofs, forthwith plays insanely the part of a dancing dervish, and, bucking about in the shafts, which are as rigid as maypoles, sets her bobbing about on her cushion like a parched pea, fluctuating indiscriminately between the hood and the splashboard, to the infinite delight of Miss Bella, who shrieks with laughter as she rides away to the band. And there she trots about among the carriages—chaffs the Colonel, promises to teach him the polka, upon which he retaliates that he has, fortunately, got a wife, and has no idea of being churned into matrimony. When away she goes, and asks old Guttler why he plays such stupid tunes, and begs he will always drop those horrid operatic airs, and give polkas, waltzes, and galops instead. She engages herself for every dance for the next ball, whenever such a contingency should chance to occur. And when the company disperse, the last departure, and the last voice we hear, are those of the merry Bella Clove.

Then we have Carry Cinnamon, who lives with Mrs. Chutney, the best and brightest of the bunch. If the crazy,

susceptible ensigns are allured by the rattling Bella, a perfect
swarm of admirers hover round the Chutneys' carriage at the
band, basking in the fair smiles, and thrilling under the
pensive glances of those large blue eyes. No, not a really
good feature does Carry possess, and yet,

> "With a wild violet grace and sweetness
> born,"

She wins all hearts; for she is so gentle and so pleasing;
admirably educated, plays nicely on the piano and harp; has
not much voice, but great taste; never affects Italian, although
she does understand it but she will sing you a simple ballad if
you really wish it. I am much mistaken if you would not like
to hear it again.

Popular rumour announces that she has rejected many a
good offer, as she declines to give her hand where her heart
cannot follow. But such a combination, it is pretty well
acknowledged, is capable, at last, of being realized, in which
case, we shall have cause to lament the loss of the most
attractive Spin of "Our Station."

Our Band

This is the Band night. Of course you will drive up and hear the Band play. I will not be so rash as to assert that you will voluntarily listen to it. But if you venture into the vicinity, you will not fail to hear it, for ours is a mightily powerful Band, that insists on making itself heard. It plays on that principle, as you can already observe by the vehemence of that operator on the big drum, and by the inflated cheeks and protruding eyes of the main body of musicians, who blow melody out of their wind-instruments.

"The gorgeous sun has sunk beneath the west," the portion of Kabob to public harmony is under the hands of the water-sprinkling "*bheestie.*" The musicians of "Ours," encased in the tightest-fitting vestments and with caps sedulously planted on the side of the black occiput by much skill and great dexterity, have marched up to the scene of fray. Herr von Guttler, the German Bandmaster, spurning the liveried dress, stalks across from his private dwelling-house. and soon after the musicians have reached the stand, he arrives in a perspiration and plain clothes, to direct the performance.

Herr von Guttler is "great nuts." He was imported from his loved fatherland for the special benefit of indoctrinating our Christian drummers in the art of music. He cannot speak a single word of English. But by much German, little French, a smattering of Hindustani, and significant gesticulations, accompanied with practical example, he is able to instil a certain amount of musical knowledge into the minds and heads of his flock. But a clever fellow in his way is Guttler. He can play every instrument in the Band, and sings a capital song, full of *Lal-lal-las*, and *shlops*, and *shlowshens*. When we have parties at our mess, and the Band plays, Herr von Guttler, after the performance, becomes a guest at the toon, or Indian mahogany, takes his claret like a man, and when the song goes round , he lets out his *Lululierties*, and his *Treenk treenk hein shlowsh mein von shlink den*, — or something like it, with wonderful velocity, which if not entirely to the comprehension of his hearers, affords, by the guttural and the inspiriting nature of the songs, a matter of lively interest and approval.

But we are forgetting the musicians. The appointed hour has come, and the Band has struck up, and plays for half an hour, for the edification of a group of children, who are in course of circulation round the stand, accompanied with their sable attendants; the occupants of Garlic's "colour-box," and Mrs. McGhee in her camel-carriage. But Herr von Guttler is absorbed with his music. He starts some operatic air. Just watch the energy with which he plays his clarionet, and how, startled with indignation at a false note by the ophecleide, he rushes round and wrings the perpetrator's ear. Then see him dart off to the drum, and show the drummer-boy how it should be played, returning the drumstick, and, to save loss of time, applying himself to his clarionet as he passes round, and ever and anon stops to administer correction with his *bâton,* or to perform some difficult passage for his pupils.

And now, as it gets dark, the lamps are lit, and the fashionable world, who have been eating the air, steer their way to the Band, to talk scandal, hear all the passing events of the day, and do anything but listen to the music. There are the Capsicums, who have always some one at their carriage. There is the Chutney turn out, and, as usual, its doors and wheels are incrusted with the devoted admirers of Miss Carry Cinnamon. There is the McGhee trap, devoid of any foreign body, and the matron bearing on her face the manifest expression of a desire for some one to come and court the gentle Barbara. There are the Turmerics, he with his legs raised on the adjacent seat, divested of his hat,.

> "Listening to the music that he heard in days
> of old,"

and favouring the visitors at his carriage with occasional references to Act 17 of 95, and Regulation 9 of 21, while Mrs. Turmeric launches out on the civil service promotion question, till her carriage is deserted, save by Huldey, who is interested in the matter. There are the Goleys, and there is Letitia talking about the moon, and there is Bella Clove, conspicuous in form and voice. And there are the carriages, the buggies, and the other vehicles of our social community. Conspicuous among them the populous shandredan of the little German Missionary, who—to fraternize for awhile with his musical countryman , with whom he is great allies—has extracted himself from the overpowering countiguity of the large Mrs. Fruitz, who smiles benignantly beneath her capacious bonnet. And why this good Mrs. Fruitz, who exercises such sound economy in worldly matters, should be so profuse in the matter of bonnets, is singularly incomprehensible. She indulges in a head-gear of mediæval character, which fertile in bows, difffuses itself with reckless extravagance in every direction. Nor must I omit the dogcart of the sporting Griff, who is practising the art of tandem-driving, to the confusion of his reins, and the signal misapprehension of his leader, who, after making an effort to annihilate the big drum, wheels round and stares very hard at his driver, inducing his partner in the shafts to co-operate in his eccentricity, and back the cart into old Mother McGhee's carriage, to her endless confusion, and the groaning dissatisfaction of her camel.

But the hours glide on, and the Band has played itself out. The decreed tunes have been perpetrated, nor can the polite Herr von Guttler be induced by the fair Bella to play even one more polka. "God save the Queen" strikes up—an air which the very horses have learned long since. At its speaking notes they prick up their ears, suddenly wake up—as do the somnolent Jehus on their boxes. The carriage-lamps are then lit, parting adieus are uttered, the vehicles gradually disperse, and thus have we experienced one more of those enlivening scenes which kill the hours of the community at "Our Station."

OUR BAND Page No. 61

OUR RACE Page No. 65

OUR COFFEE SHOP

Page No.

OUR BATH

Page No.

Our Races

Away to the far East, beyond those flaming brick-kilns which mark the boundary of "Our Station,"—there, on that plain

> "Wide and bare,
> Wide, wild, and open to the sky,"

is the far-famed racecourse of Kabob. The turf, consisting of at least three blades of auburn grass on every square foot of ground, and having the further advantage of being perforated with rat-holes as many as the stars in the firmament, copious in number as they are capacious in dimensions, the course of true racing may not be said to run entirely smooth.

The general direction is indicated by a series of posts, crowned with inverted pots of whitewashed crockery. The form is presumed to be elliptical. But as the final turn before the grand run-in bears, to my unbiassed eye, and to my personal insecurity when on the saddle, the nature of a very acute angle, I am inclined to suspect that the ellipse is of an eccentric curve, especially as my gallant gray finds a difficulty when in full speed of weathering it, without shooting involuntarily to the opposite side of the course, and exploring the field beyond—a catastrophe which, I observe, is by no means singular on his part.

The Grand Stand is an amazing structure, exhibiting the stern simplicity and severity of the primitive mound, with the advantage of the gorgeously elaborated watchtower. Here, then, is the scene of equine competition and of feats of equestrian skill. Here the rich blood of Old England's sons is proudly carried by the noble blood of Arabia's and of India's steeds. Here the fond lover delights to resort with his enamoured fair one, and

"Through the dim veil of evening's dusky
shade"

to breathe his tale of love; and here the gay world of "Our Satation" gather together at times to see the races, which the sporting community have got up for their individual improvement and the general excitement of Kabob.

This is the first day of the Sky Races, which to the uninitiated may be explained as a meeting for horses that have enjoyed no specific training beyond what could be accomplished during the interval of the "get-up" and the "come-off." On this occasion the interval has been improved to the fullest extent. The arid plain, so long deserted, has been for a fortnight a scene of stirring adventure. Here were to be seen owners of horses, in sporting habiliments, marking with knowing eyes the performances of their steeds, as they daily circulated the course and progressed to perfection. Here might be seen Godower with his pony "Tantrums," enveloped in clothing, looking like an animated feather bed. On every side were to be seen the competitors to Tantrums undergoing their matutinal rehearsals, to the delight of their respective owners.

But there goes the bugle (we don't ring vulgar bells at Kabob). The stand is crowded with the loveliest of the land. There are the Capsicums, and there is Mrs. Turmeric. There are the Chutneys, and Miss Cinnamon. But her attractions fade before the all-absorbing attractions of the hour; beauty must succumb to boots, smiles to spurs, and winning ways to whip and winning horses so her retinue is not so great. There goes Bella Clove, tearing up the course, and "declaring to win" any amount of gloves and bonnets; there are the McGhees, the Goleys, and the Ganders. Here is Huldey, who is to ride "Periwinkle" for the "Great Swelter," Beneath whose enshrouding coat may be discerned glimpses of flaming scarlet. There, beside him stands Dhotey, of sáble hue, who is to steer "Popgun" in the race—his legs, plunged into boots of irreconcilable form, bear the mighty impress of mopsticks in buckets, while a gorgeous cap of crimson adorns his head. There is Godower in ecstasies, delivering his secret instructions to Pyjamer, his Oriental jock, upon whom the honour of winning upon "Tantrums" has devolved. And only look at the spectators:—two carriages and three buggies line the rails, to which the native bipeds of Kabob have mustered to the full extent of at least five-and-twenty, and where the jolly sun-burnt gunners, who have tramped up from the barracks with their dhoodeens, alight, with their jokes and jollity quite anglicize the atmosphere.

But the bugle again sounds—they have started—there they go. It is for the "Great Swelter;" Periwinkle leading, Huldey having it all his own way; Popgun second; and then following in the ruck is Tantrums, the favourite. Here they come—the excitement is prodigious—opera-glasses in requisition-stop-watches brought into play—"Popgun" gains upon "Periwinkle"—Huldey has taken to his whip—"Tantrums" is still to the rear-the churning of horses' heads commences-the fair observers tremble with excitement.

"Periwinkle" has shut up, whip and spur are plied in vain, and with a grin of self-complacency, and amid the cheers from the brazen throats of the English soldiery, and the approving "Wah, wahs" of the indigenous, Dhotey lands "Popgun" a winner by several lenghts, and which the sagacious judge, with nose applied to the winning-post, "has been pleased to confirm."

But where is the favourite?—Why Pyjamer, the jock, received his instruction *pur et simple,* and made a "waiting" race of it, in the most literal interpretation of the phrase, to the infinite disgust of his owner, and the subsequent disfiguration of his own head. And now, while the buzz of excitement prevails, while Dhotey undergoes weighment, and the panting steeds are groomed—while the erring Pujamer receives his first tribute of jobation, and record is duly made of gloves lost and won, let us refresh ourselves, not at the hamper's side, where flows the still champagne, but at that camp-table, where coffee and cakes prevail.

And so the morning fleets away; more bugles sound, more plates are run for. There is the "Little Welter," and many more, to be competed for; in which the identical horses run, with results pretty accurately foretold. The sun mounts in the sky, and stares through a dust of gold. The last heat of the race, and the first heat of the day has "eventuated," and we all homeward wend our weary way, delighted at the races, which have for so long, and will for so long, be a subject of enlivenment at "Our Station."

Our Coffee-Shop

And of course we have a Coffee-shop! We gather together every morning after the early ride of parade, to refresh the exhausted frame with copious libations of Mocha and Bohea. There, under the shade of the Mess-house, until

> "The blazing sun that darts a downward ray,
> And fiercely sheds intolerable day,"

scatters us to our respective domiciles, we read the newspapers, expatiate in affairs in general, discuss the state of parties (dinner and musical), traffic in ideas, and while away an hour or two from the day's dull monotony, by mutual interchange of generous sentiment. Scandal is utterly discountenanced at our shop, but nevertheless (and it is a point difficult to be accounted for) there is decidedly a popular impression that prevails at "Our Station," and which signally pervades the female mind, to the effect that at that odious "Coffee-shop" the weaknesses and the frailties of mortal man, and mortal woman in particular, are daily brought to light — in a particularly strong light. The petty peculiarities and idiosyncrasies of the community are divulged and proclaimed with a startling amount of embroidery, and with a distracting deviation from rigid truth. And between ourselves, moreover, they do say that whatever gets to the ear of the Coffee-shop, is disseminated and thoroughly made known, at every point of "Our Station," with signal and inconceivable rapidity, the facts gaining perceptibly as they circulate, to the furtherance of the romantic.

But in all this "Our Coffeep-shop" is grievously libelled. We recognize in it the manifestation of a too bilious temperament—the explosion of an over-sensitive, if not evil-minded, disposition. Veracity, however, compels me to say that the philosophical and scientific subjects of discourse are unquestionably seasoned at time with episodes of domestic life, and that, amidst dissertations upon the arts of war, the arts of "Mamma" are occasionally evolved; military movements draw one unconsciously to the manœuvring movements of mothers. The attack of intrenched camps leads irrresistibly to the winning of intrenched hearts. Offering terms to the garrison suggests naturally a proposal to marry; operations of an army in the field, to the operations in a domestic household; whilst the intelligence of what is going on in the wide, wide world, as revealed in the newspapers, leads to the intelligence of what goes on in the narrow limits of our benighted homes.

And thus it was that the subject of surgical operations in the jaw educed the intelligence, at this morning's Coffee-shop, that Nicaldo, the itinerant dentist, had arrived at Kabob, and that Mrs. McGhee, whose teeth, numerically as well as positively, had "dwindled to their shortest span," had the balance summarily extracted, and that Nicaldo is engaged to supply new ones, which have already been designated "Mother

McGhee's new dinner-set." This circumstance naturally led to the extravagance of the lady implicated, inasmuch as old McGhee had been seen that morning at the auction-sale of poor Sergeant Trail, and that he purchased for the sum of two rupees eleven annas, three flannel waistcoats, five pair of socks, and an old toothbrush,—all of which he carried home in his hat; and that he frowned so hard at the bugler boys that they were afraid to bid against him—sufficiently proving his character is favourable to economy.

Then we hear the opinions that are expressed relative to the last night's "feed' at the Gander'; how the ham, professedly a "prime York," had been distinctly traced as having had its origin in the ravine that skirts the lovely Kabob; and that fellow Garlic insists upon it that he saw, with his own naked eye, the native vendor of swine disposing of his produce to Mrs. Gander in her verandah. Moreover, we discover that the turkey was the leanest old bird in creation, and that its breast was puffed out by the ingenious introduction of a tough old fowl, but which the keen eye of Pullow detected.

Then we are told of the hop last night at the Guddurs', which was pronounced to be "deadly lively." The heat was so great that Mrs. Chunam, who, as it is declared, has eleven pence out of the shilling of Hindoo blood floating in her veins, and who delights to veneer as much of herself as is exposed to public view, for the purpose of the whitening of her otherwise shady complexion—the heat, we understand, was so great, that the veneer cracked and peeled off in flakes. And further, that her dress happening to subside from off her shoulders, a lovely olive rim, where the veneer had not been applied, became visible, for the general edification.

Guddur, of "Ours," then narrates his adventure in the dance with Barbara, who travelled about the room like a paviour's rammer, to the detriment of his feet and knees. And we also ascertain that Miss Goley favoured the company with a song all about a "bonnie coo,"—which Guddur declared was a hymn, or at any rate a roundelay, while Pullow bets him a new hat that it was a Caledonian melody of an agricultural character.

Thus it is clearly manifest that at "Our Coffee-shop" there is no such thing as scandal, but the simple recording of pure authenticated facts. And thus, with the aid of coffee and cheroots, newspapers, and perhaps a game at billiards in the adjoining room, we while away the fleeting hour, form plans for the coming day, and then, as the sun waxes warm, we migrate to the Bath, which, next to the Coffee-shop, is decidedly one of the most popular scenes of resort at "Our Station."

Our Bath

Nor are we without the charm of a fashionable watering-place, whither the gay resident of Kabob may resort, to enjoy the luxury of bathing, relieved for a while from the oppression of the

"Busy town's tumultuous crowds,"

absolved from the rigid formalities of urban life, and where he can indulge in the glorious liberty of the subject by an unrestricted freedom of attire.

But our watering-place is an exceptive one; it is not situated on the shore of the wide-spreading ocean,

"Where all agree
With one consent to rush into the sea."

Nor are our eyes gladdened by the prospect of a lovely woman basking on the glittering shingle, listening to the plash of the receding wave, and watching with attentive eye the sunburnt mariner, or the snowy sail of the bonnie bark as she rides on the waters blue.

We have not our pea-green seats of gridiron build, on
which delight to sit those virgin forms of loveliness absorbed
in wide-spreading hats and the latest novel. We have not our
groups of rosy-cheeked, laughing children to trundle their
intractable hoops against our legs, or to project their
incorrigible shuttlecocks into our unoffending eyes. We do
not rejoice in chaises with quadrupeds that have acquired the
art of compassing the very smallest extent of ground in their
hour's trot. Nor have we troupes of Jerusalem ponies,
garnished with their draperied saddles, wrought into a canter
by the impulsive donkey-boys, and bearing on their belaboured
backs the merriest of dear England's fair ones.

These things are not in the nature of our watering-place.
Ours is charmingly situated on the shores of the waterless
nullah that bisects Kabob. The water where the delights of
the bath are effected does not come with its rolling waves
plashing on a sand-girt shore, but trickles from an adjoining
well, from whence it has been forced by the unremitting
energies of horned cattle, and where it plashes (when
disturbed) against the plastered sides of a brick-built reservoir.

This is our watering-place of Kabob, in which the form of
woman — lovely woman — is never seen. Where the male
species, with all the seclusion of a Parliament House, have its
enjoyment entirely to themselves. Let us betake ourselves to
the festive scene; the trip, the change of air, the bath, will
revive our falling nature.

We find a bungalow of one large room, with its floor
scooped out for the reception of the enticing fluid. We find
ourselves plunged into a vortex of human society. It is the
season, the very height of the season, and all the fashionble
world of Kabob, of the masculine gender, have flocked hither —
the early risers from their morning ride, the later risers from
their sleepless cots. The Coffee-shop has yielded its ample

store, and the votaries of Mocha and Bohea, with the subsidiary libations of gossip and of "jaw," have one and all become the votaries of the water and Companions of the Bath.

Here, on the left, is Scrape Doss reaping the beard of some hirsute visitor. See with what dexterity he wields the razor Mark how its polished edge is whetted by its rapid application to his bared and honelike arm. Observe the velocity with which the snowy lather is laid on, and then more rapidly removed (the patient's nose acting as a helm, by which the motions of the pliant chin are guided by the skilful excisor). And look how the jovial crew disport themselves in the water—how they

"Plunge about like porpoises or whales at play."

But what is the prime agent of their fun? A water-carrier's bag!—the inflated hide of some immolated sheep, which is formed into a Neptune's car, and upon which it becomes an object of ambition to learn the art of equitation—an art which combines the difficulties of the saddle with the posing peculiarities of the tight-rope. The simplest thing in the world is to ride upon a "mussock"—just like swimming and skating, when you know how to effect it—but a most incorrigible thing is a "mussock" to an early learner. It is so detestably buoyant, nothing will induce it to let you mount,—no ticklish steed was ever so unmanageable. But you get the better of it, stride across it, and, skilfully balanced, grip its sides, determined to fall neither to the right hand nor to the left; when the remorseless monster slips away backward from beneath you, and you are plunged headlong into the foaming water; or it springs upward at the bows, and in your ignominious fall, while the circling wave closes over your eyes, and your hair and the water are removed from your eyes, you detect the object of your immersion floating impenitently, and with a sort of sidelong glance of derision, right at the other end of the Bath.

Look at the essayists—those youthful aspirants for "mussock" honours in every stage of acquired skill. Here is one who, to an unimpassioned and unbiassed observer, the "mussock" might certainly be pronounced to be invariably the rider, and not the ridden. There, on that side, are veterans in the art, who have converted their Neptune's cars into men of war, and with energy and vigour contest for the supremacy of the wave. Here are incipient swimmers, endeavouring to overcome that fatal facility for sinking involuntarily to the bottom. There the more experienced, who have acquired the elementary knowledge of the art, and who are in a delectable state of mind at being able to remain on the surface, are floating joyfully about, but occasionally becoming the victims of contending factions, and getting ducked. There, on the banks, are those who have disported themselves sufficiently, and are being groomed and rubbed down by their attendant slaves.

But we have joined in the morning's *divertissement*—we have laughed, we have been splashed, we have been shaven, and we have been dressed. And now, as the sun is frightfully hot, we will have the hood of our buggy put up, and rattle home to breakfast, feeling for a time invigorated, and rejoicing to know that we have the opportunity afforded to us of enjoying the luxury of a watering-place at "Our Station."

Our Sporting Griff

The young blood of Kabob has its sporting representative in the form of the verdant Godower — a youth precocious in horseflesh, and exuberant in his own animal development. Released from the rod of his oppressor at school, he has been shipped to the land of Ind as food for powder, bearing with him a love of the equine species imbibed from his exercitation on the nursery rocking-horse and from his occasional visits to some neighbouring races.

The mind of the sporting Griff exhibits innocence of a virginal character, from which he becomes the source of much enlivenment to his fellow-subs, who vent their superfluous jocosity by playing their pranks with this simple and unsophisticated youth. But our Griff has a right good temper, and enjoys the fun: he is game for anything, joins in everything that savours of sport — has learnt to smoke, and polishes off his bottle of beer, or his brandy-and-water, in a style that would refreshen his good old mother to behold.

Our Griff has established a stud. His advent among us was, as usual, the signal for the concentration at his garden-gate of every pony in the Bazar, whose owners, eager to sell, were pressing upon him to purchase, with irresistible argumentations, backed by the exhibition of the performances of each individual animal. The temptation was not to be overcome and our Griff became the happy possessor of a diminutive *tat* (as we designate the ponies in the East), resplendent with an orange-coloured tail and orangecoloured legs, which his previous owner, a corpulent Baboo, had had dyed in true Oriental fashion.

There is Godower. He lives in that corner bungalow, chumming with half a dozen other Griffs. You see, he is just going to parade and his faithful valet is giving the last finishing touches to complete his martial perfectness, by hooking that intractable collar, which he finds some difficulty in seeing or reaching. There, behind him, is his table attendant, bringing to his master the matutinal cup of tea, which our Griff has already learned to indulge in. But our Griff is hurried, and the tea is hot, which accounts for the simple expedient resorted to by the faithful domestic, to render it practicable for immediate bibition. And there is the gallant *tat*, which, from its ambiguity of temper, its retrograde tendencies, and other inexplicable peculiarities, has been christened "Tantrums" by its sporting owner, who has at last accomplished for himself the pleasing art of riding the obstreperous little brute, whose activity, on frequent occasions, resulted in ejecting its ruler and guide from the precincts of the saddle. But our Griff, gifted with rude determination, would slope away to the confines of cantonment, and there, "remote from public view" and the chaff of his fellow-subs, acquire dexterity in the management of the steed, and in securing for himself permanency of occupation in the saddle.

Look at the little "Tantrums!" His diminutive size is not entirely adapted for the large English saddle and bridle which a fond mother and a liberal outfitter had exported with him.

But there are to be races at Kabob. Our Griff, judging from the fleet movements of the little "Tantrums," when on a late occasion he involuntarily eloped with his unapproving master, and bore him swiftly over hill and dale, until he reached the object of his affections—his gram-bag—judging from his rapidity on that occasion, our Griff considers him well suited for the turf, and accordingly little "Tantrums" is entered for the "Great Swelter," and is forthwith put into the elementary stage of training. To see our Griff directing the performance is quite refreshing; to see little "Tantrums" smothered in blankets, undergoing the operation of having his superfluous flesh reduced—daily fining down, to the approval of his master—is delightful. Then to see our Griff count the number of gulps that "Tantrums" drank, which were duly decreed, was delicious. But, finer still, to see with what gusto he banged the nigger's head for giving one gulp in excess. Then to see the grooming, the enveloping, the girthing, and, finally, the despatching homewards of the visibly attenuated "Tantrums," was superlatively encouraging.

But our Griff has his own jock. For, having serious objections to castor-oil and blankets for a reduction of his own weight, which could never by any possibility be lowered to suit the inches of his courser, he engaged the services of one Pyjamer, an Oriental breaker-in of horses, who was immediately installed in his office and top boots. But our Griff's sporting propensities rest not here. He has been seduced into combining with a brother sub in establishing a vehicle and apparatus, representing a six-dozen chest on a pair of gigantic wheels, which bears the character of a perambulating a watch-tower, but called a dog-cart, from the summit of which, accessible only to those who venture to imperil their lives in the ascent, the view of the horse's back and the surrounding country at large becomes faint and indistinct. In this apparatus our Griff pays his morning calls. Where he has been can be clearly discovered by the discomfited state of the gate-posts, which have uniformly shed bricks on his approach and the contiguous drain-bridges, which have been bereft of their parapets. Occasionally the valour of our Griff, and his love of adventure, is exhibited by the addition of a supplementary horse in front, by way of tandem, which operates as effectually as the plague in clearing the highways. The obstinacy of that leader is thoroughly known, and its pertinacity in resisting all appeals to go where it ought is strikingly manifest to every one on the Mall. It is considered a relief when our Griff, as he always does, gets his apparatus away on to the Parade to turn round. As such an intricate movement could never be effected within the narrow boundaries of the Mall.

And here we must leave him, and pronounce him to be a "jolly Griff," the favourite of his brother subs, the friend of all, and a source of much fun and enlivenment to the community of "Our Station."

OUR GRIFF Page No. 77

OUR MOONSHEE Page No. 81

OUR BURRA KHANA Page No. 85

OUR PACK OF HOUNDS Page No. 8

Our Moonshee

Who lives in that next bungalow, with the Indo-Grecian portico? Why, Dhalbhat of Ours—as good a fellow as ever speared a pig or loved a lassie. Nice-looking house! Yes; and Dhalbhat knows how to keep it cool, too, having gleaned some "wrinkles" from the Colonel. I rather suspect Dhalbhat would take unto himself a wife, if Kabob could produce one to his fancy· (he had an eye for Carry Cinnamon, but he knows that Cheeny is in the field before him, and is coming in an easy winner), for his house is all ready for the reception of a Mrs. Dhalbhat, with its round table, and couches, whose

"Soft solicitations court repose;"

its marble-topped side-tables, its easy-chairs, and such things, which are prophetic of a state of connubial domesticity approximate or anticipated.

We couldn't get on without Dhalbhat: he manages the mess, is sectetary of the book-club, our best bowler at cricket, a first-rate racket-player, and a stunning good dancer, an excellent actor, a keen sportsman, a capital musician, up to any sport and fun. But his colloquial acquirements in the Oriental tongue are of rather a restricted nature, and his attainments in the "black classics" are about as great as his admiration for the Oriental race is microsopic.

Dhalbhat, however, has taken to his books, as the Chief has promised to give him an appointment on his staff if he passes the examination; so he is endeavouring to struggle some Hindustani into his brains, which is no easy joke, I can tell you, for a man who "hates the niggers".

Come into his house; I suspect you will find him at it now, with that fat old baghobahar, the Moonshee. A famous Moonshee is Baghobahar! and a capital hand at coaching you along, and getting you through the examinatioin, although the rascal can't speak a word of English. If you wish to distinguish yourself, I recommend you to enlist him in your service, and enter into a solemn contract and agreement with him, that if you on your part do, zealously, and without any interruption, attend to the instruction imparted by him for a certain number of hours per diem, which is the usual arrangement, he on his part will undertake to infuse such an amount of Oriental knowledge into your pericranium as will enable you to emerge from the examination-hall a passed man. For this instillation of the Oriental tongue, you further agree to remunerate him to a certain extent monthly, and to bestow upon him as a donation, the whole of the Government grant to which you then become legitimately entitled to.

I strongly suspect that our friend Baghobahar finds that his pupil does slightly infringe the former portion of his contract, and that the unwavering and undiverted attention is not unfrequently interrupted by the intrusion of beer, soda-water, and brandy, and other such impediments to the current of thought. While an occasional inundation of kindred spirits, on frolic bent, flows into the student's chamber, and mars the serenity of the lesson by irrelevant proceedings, to the indignation of old Baghobahar, who views them evidently as a society for the confusion of useful knowledge.

There, as I told you, is our friend at his studies. That terrible guttural, which he is striving to pronounce, sticks in his throat, and necessitates an appeal for assistance to the bottle of brandy which the slave is about to uncork, a few drops of which, to tinge the water that is to come out of that goblet on the ground, will no doubt lubricate the offending thorax.

But Baghobahar crosses his stockinged feet, and calculates that, with all the divergences of Dhalbhat's attention, and with all the hinderance of but little knowledge of the language having been ingrafted into him, he will still be able to coach him through. A capital hand at lying in ambush is Baghobahar, and for rattling off an exercise for a disconsolate pupil. Fudge, of the Fire-eaters, employed him as his Moonshee, and when he went up to pass he could scarcely read the character. But he was an ingenious dog, had a secret volume scientifically illuminated, which enabled him to read off his passages with fluency and precision. And then for his exercise, by the expedient of a conspirator in the shape of a slave, who was apparently a mere conveyer of a glass of water, but who bore away clandestinely a note of hand, the Moonshee, who was in ambuscade without, honoured it at sight, and the exercise, promptly done, was furtively introduced once more, presented to the examiners, and Fudge became a passed man.

Chutney was president of the last committee, and a precious particular hand he is, I can tell you,—always on the look-out that you don't get to windward of him, always hovering disgustingly about you, and peering over your shoulder, as Muggins calls it, and seeing that you don't filch your exercises. But Turmeric is pronounced to be a "brick," as he doesn't bother himself with leaving his chair, and, his range of vision being limited, he can't "twig" all the ingenious devices brought into play to remove the horrible difficulties put before one. But, sharp as Chutney is, Fudge managed to overreach him. Everybody is not a Fudge, however!

Baghobahar thinks that, by a similar style of procedure, he may land Dhalbhat safely on the other side, and be the happy recipient of the long-anticipated grant.

We have other Moonshees at Kabob, some who speak English. But as far as a knowledge of the different Oriental languages, and a skill and facility in imparting them to others is concerned, Baghobahar is unquestionably the best Moonshee at "Our Station."

Our Burra Khanah

"   My Dear Captain Quiz,
      "*Do* induce your newly-arrived friend to accompany you to-night, and give us the pleasure of his company at dinner. We shall be *so* delighted to see him.

"Believe me always *very* sincerely yours,

"ISABELLA BYLE"

There, now, an invitation to dinner!—to a "Burra Khanah," literally a grand feed; one of the periodical explosions for which the Byles are celebrated, as it gratifies simultaneously the animal appetites of the guests and the sociable propensities of Mrs. Byle, who prefers these wholesale entertainments, these general amalgamation spreads, as productive of a great amount of effect. They are invariably celebration feasts, to record some important domestic event, as the anniversary of their wedding, birthdays, and the like. And this spread is to inaugurate the introduction of a tender Byle into this world of woe, which took place last month, and the christening came off this morning.

Byle, as you are aware, is a gunner, and commands the Cow Battery. A jolly fellow is Byle. A terrific sportsman, always prowling about the ravines after tigers, and sitting up all night, perched upon crazy structures of bamboo, lying in wait for leopards, bears, hyenas, and such-like small game. Mrs. Byle is a splendid rider, and ready for any fun, thinks nothing of her five-and-twenty miles before breakfast, often joins Byle on his elephant when he goes tiger-shooting, and would go into action with the guns as soon as take her evening canter.

Delightful people, the Byles! But the truth must be told: these grand spreads are cruelly ponderous, and indigestible to the feelings—those awful periods between the heats—that stifling room, with the incense of savoury meats (which lie in hecatombs on the table) hanging about like a London fog, which the punkah fails to disperse.

But stay; the company have assembled—there they are, ranged in a semicircle with a formidable degree of precision, from which the male species, ever nervous, have shrunk with apparent dread, and have subsided into platoons at the doorways, and are awaiting the advent of the dinner with silent expectancy.

Byle has sallied forth, for the fifteenth time at least, to expedite the movements of the table attendants, and fearful threats of summary vengeance are floated into our ears. Mrs. Byle is chatting away to her nearest guests, and endeavouring to inject some happiness into them; occasionally suggesting that Byle should solicit the exercise of a little expedition on the part of the domestics; and when Byle has sallied forth, for the sixteenth time, then is the comforting intimation announced that the dinner is on the table, to the unmitigated satisfaction of the guests and the intense relief of the worthy hostess.

The procession is then formed. Away goes Byle with the

"Burra Beebee,' who on this occasion is Mrs. Chutney, and Mrs. Byle appropriating Fitznoodle, the "order of their going" (a matter of an intricate nature, involving references to an Army List) is pointed out, or fearful would be the consequences. For, as we all know, the Turmerics are cuts with the Cardamoms, and Mrs. McGhee is at variance with Mrs. Koofter, and the Chutneys don't speak to the Gabys, and the Guddahs are at social enmity with the Ganders; and a few others are cuts with a few more; and all because of previous inaccuracies and wilful divergences in matters of precedence.

But the dinner is, at last, set fairly going; the host and hostess occupy their respective centres of the table, while the top and bottom, with their appalling concomitant consequences of turkey and ham to carve, are studiously shunned, and become the refuge for the Griff, who in this sphere of action imbibes his earliest lessons in carving.

But the time would fail me to tell of how the feast progresses. Indefatigable are the slaves in catering for their masters' wants, and eager in the pursuit of the choicest dishes, and vigorous in their contests for the cool champagne-which limpid beverage has had the charm of rousing the dull echoes; for now the conversation flows apace. Chumuch, the Griff, dissects the turkey, but consigns a pound and a half of stuffing into the velvet lap of the adjoining Mrs. Koofter. The flounce of the punkah becomes partly disengaged, and, after flapping about remorselessly like an unreefed sail in a gale of wind, succeeds in whisking off the protecting wire-gauze top of the lamp, and launching it on the apex of Miss Goley's head, occasioning the blowing-out of the lamp, and the consequent oleaginous effluvium that proceeds from the expiring wick, to the general discomposure of the nasal organs. Then the punkah had to be stopped to undergo reparation; and frantic and awful is the heat that is engendered thereby.

Then, after an interregnum of considerable duration, the second course is produced, succeeded by a pause "more fearful than before."

The sweets have vanished, and at last the dessert, indicative of a concluding climax. The decanters are circulated, and the fair hostess telegraphs to the "Burra Beebee" the signal for departure, and a move (in the right direction) is made.

Then the gentlemen are doomed to a further session, which terminates in the production of coffee, when the gong tells its tale of midnight. The piano is heard in the adjoining room; some faint voice warbles a doleful strain, the "Burra Beebee" rises, and a general dispersion ensues.

Thus have we conspired with the good Mrs. Byle in the inauguration "blow-out;" we have drunk to her health in an early glass of cool champagne, and that of the baby Byle in a later bottle of a more tepid character. We have imbibed and feasted upon the good things that were piled upon her mahogany. But the heat of the room, we are thoroughly convinced, has deprived us of a stone of our natural weight. But we have peculiar predilections, and do not recognize in her "Burra Khanah" the most cheerful or the most delectable occupation to be experienced for the enlivement of an evening at "Our Station."

Our Pack of Hounds

I should rather think we did enjoy the pleasures of the chase at "Our Station," and that Kabob can boast of the luxury of a music-giving pack! Only rise from your "downy couch recumbent" to-morrow morning, when it is pitch-dark,—for the meet takes places at daybreak with thrilling punctuality,—when you shall witness the performances of as glorious a kennel as ever roused the welkin with sweet voices musical. Ours is a subscription pack, literally and absolutely,—a term ascribed, not from the mere paltry subscription of vulgar coin for its existence and support, but from the generous subscription, as a temporary arrangement by their sporting owners, of the very dogs themselves, which, on the announcement of a meet, duly and authentically made known in the columns of the *Kabob Chronicle*, and the better-digested pages of the regimental order-books, are forthwith deputed to attend. Thus, from the four corners of Kabob, the contributions of the canine species, in pleasing variety, are to be seen, panting for the chase, and migrating to the appointed meet.

Harriers, foxhounds, staghounds, beagles? — Not entirely. Terriers, Scottish and of Skye; spaniels, with retrieverish and retrogressive tendencies; bulldogs, of sinister aspect, and with irreconcilable legs; greyhounds, greedy and gaunt; together with a miscellaneous assortment of indescribables, rejoicing in unabbreviated ears, and ambiguous in their genealogy, compose the heterogeneous pack.

Hark, the shrill clarion sounds, and there comes Geedur the huntsman.

> "Garnish'd for the chase, the gallant Sub
> To these lone plains directs his devious
> way."

See how well the pack are kept in hand, for the retentive chain and collar are still unloosed, and the sable keepers restrain the clamorous hounds, which scent the odorous game; for in that covert, that close, that thick-set covert, which lies upon the coolie's head, is the object of the coming pursuit. We spurn the irksome delays of the search for game. No beating of the bush, no crushing through the dense copses to expel the artful fox or timorous hare. Be ours the glories of the stag-hunt, the ready-made, the never-missing game; there — there in that thicket, in that basket, I should say — lies the already scented jackal, scented at an unlimited expenditure of turpentine; and there is a duplicate, to forestall the possibility of a too speedy capture and a lack of sport.

The performance of "throwing off" is forthwith commenced, by the throwing off of the basket from the Oriental's head. Warily, by reason of a due regard for the operator's fingers, is the encaged jackal released, and sulkily he avails himself of the privilege of leave. The yelpings of the pack warn him, however, that danger is nigh, and, with a furtive glance, he sees the flashing eye of Pincher and the glistening teeth of Bruno, and he improves the occasion by a more speedy retreat. The "field" have now joined: there is Huldey (desirous to see the performances of the little Forceps), more sportingly attired than ever; there is Godower, in gorgeous array-leathern tights, wrought from an old pair of horse-artilleryman's breeches; there is Jootey, who appears in undeniable tops, auburn in complexion, and redolent of calf; there is Grambags, in his embroidered staff cap, and sporting the military spur (Grambags must advertise he is on the Staff, and no longer a parade-crusher); then there goes Legarm, less regardful of appearances, in a flannel jacket and mushroom hat. But the bugle-note of prerparation has shrilled, and it fails me to tell of Jeen and of Ginger, of Kirrich and of Garlick, of Chumuch and of Kanter, and the rest of the sporting lot. The dogs are let loose. They sniff the pungent turpentine, and away they go with fleeting step and swift. The pace is dreadfully severe, right across the Parade, down to the banks of the sandy stream, whose waterless bed, glimmering in the dawn, is radiant with swine; when, saddening to tell, schism and dissent enter into the pack.

Heedless of the alluring turpentine, insensate to the appeals and objurgation of the huntsmen, the truant pack run riotous. A maternal pig with her domestic progeny in train is singled out by Pincher and his party, whilst Caesar and his immediate followers devote their undivided attention to an aggrieved grunter. The gallant little Forceps has succumbed under the lash of his infuriated master, and taken immediate steps for a bolt home, while the rermainder of the pack stand by, indiscriminately wavering on the banks, and give vent to their unqalified approval in unsophisticated bark.

The hopes of the huntsmen are fled, the jackal has got off scot-free, and the gasping, panting keepers, now running up, appropriate severally their respective batch of dogs. The fresh basket with the fresh jackal, and the pack, now brought into subjection, are moved off to a distant spot, where their attention may be undiverted; a fresh start is made, the jackal on this occasion not let out of sight, the hounds go in with a rush, the game makes for Cantonments, and, after a crushing run of exactly three minutes and a quarter, a seizure is made, and jackal receives his quietus.

The sun has now mounted the sky, the field disperses, the dogs are taken to their respective homes, and the subject of the morning's sport and the awful run, with but slight allusions to the pig episode, are the subjects of discussion at the coffee-shop in the morning, at the band in the evening, and the enlivenment throughout the day of the community of "Our Station."

Our Ball

Kabob is in convulsions! Kabob is in a state of agitation—of excitement—that can and will only be relieved by some severe and vigorous operation!

The young blood of Kabob has run riot, and the symptoms manifested are of such a nature as to need some active treatment, which it is proposed to administer in the form of a Station Ball. The Terpsichoreans of Kabob have well-nigh lost the gifted faculty of the dance. The patent-leather boots and the white satin shoes have been lying fallow for many a long and weary day; while the kid-gloves, though

"Lost to sight, to memory dear,"

have been in a state of unsullied retirement in the custody of slaves.

It is true that an occasional carpet dance has ever and anon aroused the votaries of the "mazy," and the even connubial combinations have flowed from the petty quadrillings, and polkings at the domestic shrine; but the walls of the Kabob Assembly Rooms have long been mute, resounding and reverberating no crash of the dance-inspiring band. Those chandeliers, those wall-lights, with their crystal shelterings, have become the home of the spider; while the lizard rambles fearlessly along those dormant punkahs, that have for so many a day remained quiescent.

But "the spell is past, the dream is o'er." Its walls are resonant again with the sounds of jollity and preparation. The sable pagan has started into activity, and the dusty chandeliers once more glitter in their joy. The crimson-edged flounces of the punkahs, fresh from the hands of the *blanchisseur,* glimmer with spotless purity. The stewards, indefatigable fellows, defiant of all heat, devote themselves to the rigid lacing-up of the floor-cloth; and the once bare walls, with their sickly hue of pale yellow-wash, are now gay and verdant with wreaths, and other incrustations of foliage, so artfully devised and skilfully applied; while radiant stars of glittering swords and bayonets, with the regimental colours splendidly conspicuous, likewise decorate and adorn the walls.

But let us escape awhile from the scene of the coming fray, and betake ourselves to the Cantonments. The Ball is a general subscription one, and prodigious is the excitement at the forthcoming event. Chouse Lall is pre-eminently conspicuous; his big bundles have had to disgorge their artificial flowers, and a general desire for gloves has terminated in a clearance of his supply. Mrs. Jootmoot's establishment has been assailed for the immediate propagation of dresses; while the tailors of Kabob, and Mrs. Capsicum's gang to boot, have stitched for their very lives, amidst perfect clouds of muslin, of tarlatan, and of crape.

But the hour has come —8, 9, 10 have sounded on the gong, —the lights are lit, the torches flicker at the gate, buggies roll into the portico, and the fair ones begin to drop in. The arrival of one —a second —and then a brace —establishing a quartette—justifies the immediate opening of the Ball. The music strikes up, and a quadrille is fairly under way.

But, see, fresh arrivals have added to the hilarity of the scene! The doors, thronged with red and blue jackets, whose possessors, hoping against hope (for the best dancers have all been engaged a good week ago), lie in wait to prey upon some fair one who, through some fortuitous circumstance and the wheel of Fortune, might haply be disengaged; and who, with the inspiration of the music, and with desperate resolve, are determined, rather than miss the dance, to have a polka in combination even with the foot-crushing Goley, whose general misapprehension of the art tends rather to limit the applications for her partnership in the dance, and who, in consequence, has not received so many anticipatory invitations. Letitia becomes, then, an easy prey to the forlorn.

But the band has started a *deux temps*. There, in the giddy whirl, you see the gentle Barbara, her orbicular face radiant with delight, and plunging about like a dolphin in blue; there is the sportive Bella; there is the graceful Carry Cinnamon, who can dance, I promise you, as Cheeny of "Ours," who is waltzing with her, can testify; and there—ye Gods! look at that intruding Oriental, unendowed with over-much drapery, and with a soul set upon punkahs, stalking complacently across the arena. Now, I ask if a gentle corrective is not desirable and which, if I mistake not, that steward by the door is more than likely to administer.

But the waltzes, the polkas, the schottisches, and the quadrilles are, in time, resolved into the "Roast Beef of England;" the supper-room doors are opened, and the ballroom is deserted, save by the pea-green form of Mrs. McGhee, who sits wrecked on her seat, until some humane steward, descrying her, launches forth and lands her in the supper-room, and revives her with a tumbler of champagne. Turkeys

and hunter's beef, fowls, jellies, and blancmange—as usual,
interspersed with crackers and the opening of bottles—are
now the matters of all-absorbing interest.

The supper is over, the band strikes up, the dancing
recommences, another hour or two glide away, till the couples
lag and loiter in the dance, the music becomes irrelevant in
nature, the lamps begin to flicker, and the wall-flowers to
nod—the carriages drive up, and the guests depart.

A fresh invasion is made upon the supper-table by the
survivors, a general disinvestment of jackets ensues, pegs
and cheroots inspire vocal melody, until the morning-sun
announces the break of day, and the spirits of the Ball depart.

Thus has Kabob signalized itself by this great event; the
Ball is pronounced to have been most successful, and well
attended; for there were at least nine ladies, five of whom
could dance. It is true that many a fair face is missed; but
there are domestic occurrences which occasionally militate
against participation in such hilarities, as Mrs. Goodrey, the
monthly nurse—who might have been engaged seventeen
times this month—can satisfactorily attest. But, yet we are all
delighted, and look forward with bright hopes to a repetition
of the same, to cheer the society of "Our Station."

OUR BALL Page No. 93

OUR TIGER SHOOTING Page No. 97

OUR STAGE-COACHING Page No. 10

OUR AGRICULTURISTS Page No. 1

Our Tiger-Shooting

And we do something in the shooting line at Kabob; though the small game are scarcely worth the exertion of tramping after, being at rather an inconvenient distance. We can, of course, go out and knock over our dozen or two brace of blacks (partridges I mean, not niggers), and snipe as many as we choose to blaze away at, to say nothing of hares and all sorts of small fry, when in season. Yet who cares for such cock-robin sort of shooting after having been accustomed to polishing off a tiger or two before breakfast, and bagging a few leopards, bears, and such-like before tiffin?

You would like to try your luck at tiger-shooting? Of course you would: what English schoolboy with a soul for a popgun would not? There is the experienced Byle, with a pericranium like a walnut, which the sun can't crack, who will give you a lesson, and under his tutelage I engage you will be shown some sport. Of course, you will be exposed to the sun, and perhaps to the water too. Think of Byle: the other day, in his little encounter with a tiger, on his last expedition; the elephant upon which he was riding, feeling the claws of the tiger rather unpleasantly intrusive on his hind quarters—just as you might dispporove of the claws of a great tom-cat penetrating your own thigh—ignominiously took to flight, rushed past the edge of a tank full of water, under a tree, a bough of which caught the howdah, which from the impetus at which the elephant was doing his back-steps, was swept off, dropping Byle into the water, which, fortunately, was only five feet deep. The tiger also lost his place by this sweeping measure, and fell on the bank. There he stood, being about as fond of water as a cat, and being pretty sure of his prey; while Byle, with his head only out of the tank, as you see a buffalo in a river, stood staring at him in turn; and thus they remained for hours under a broiling sun till a party came to the rescue—Byle reached the other side, got a gun, went back into a good position, and then and there, while swimming, lodged a rifle-ball in the tiger's head.

Now, you may have a chance to-day of doing the same: for this morning an aggrieved agriculturist came howling into the cantonments, reporting the sudden apparition of a tiger, only fifteen miles off, which had abstracted his oxen and his fatlings, and evinced a desire, moreover, to elope with his wife. So Byle has got his battery—not the Cow Battery, but the private battery of guns—fieldpieces you may call them if you like, or, at any rate, fowling-pieces and rifles. Topey has lent some elephants, a troop of beaters have been enlisted, and we shall be off in the morning by daybreak. The elephants go out to-night, and we go to cover on our hacks.

Byle frequently faces his tigers on foot, but I don't recommend you to do that. Unless you can guarantee your nerves not flinching in a time of imminent danger. And let me tell you the nervous system is not at all unlikely to suffer temporary derangement at being made a Van Amburgh without any preliminary preparation, and placed suddenly in the immediate presence of a "Royal Bengal" without the interposition of the menagerie railings.

But the morning gun has fired. Our valet has roused us from our hard cot and our soft slumbers. We have quaffed our Bohea, mounted our Arabs, and galloped to the scene of action. The elephants are all prepared, with their sporting howdahs duly stocked with their batteries. The afflicted agriculturist is there, and points out with looks of anguish "the vestiges of [the tiger's] creation," in the shape of the bones of his favoured bullock, which the famished tiger then and there devoured, as we see some watery-mouthed schoolboy devouring, at the pastrycook's door, the tartlets he had thought to carry home, but which hunger and a wistful eye could not resist. We listen to his tale of woe, hear that two more bullocks have been abstracted, and we promise the full value of all, and of many more, if he will but show us the tiger.

Away then we start. With cunning eye the beaters track the foot-prints in the shade. He has got into jungle, and now the track is lost. The beaters form in line; Byle leads in the centre, while Dhalbhat and Muggins are on the left, Huldey and Godower on the right, and a few more. Away we go; we strain our eyes in every direction; occasionally we have a false alarm, then the elephants turn up their trunks, and go trumpeting along, crushing down the jungle—at times into the deep ravines, into which they lower their huge bodies so carefully and so well, then clambering up again, press onward on their way. A beater gives a shout—he is on the track—he sees blood upon the trampled grass! The sun has begun to shoot down his penetrating rays upon our turbaned heads, which need the still greater protection of the umbrella. Another shout! Byle, with a practical eye, judges where the game may be, points to our friend the agriculturist, who is beside his elephant, where he should explore. A yell, accompanied by a precipitate flight on the part of the bereaved Oriental, followed by a roar from the tiger, and two sharp cracks from a double rifle, announces to the field that the game has been found.

The bullets have struck the tiger, but not fatally. He crashes into the jungle before Byle can take up a second gun, and springs in his rage on to the tail of Dhalbhat's elephant, which, unaccustomed to such sports, being simply a baggage-elephant enlisted for the occasion, had wheeled about with inconceivable rapidity at the first roar of the tiger, and was preparing for an ignominious flight, when he was tackled from behind. But a ball from Dhalbhat drops the tiger from his hold, who then receives a third broadside from Huldey's gun. By this time, the mahout of Byle's elephant has brought him round, and, with two more carefully-directed shots, Byle gives the tiger his quietus.

The victim is hoisted on to a pad elephant, we refresh ourselves with the necessary beverages, our elephants tramp back with us to the rendezvous, we mount our Arabs, and gallop to cantonments in time for tiffin, delighted and properly baked in our morning's amusement, and long to hear of another tiger having ventured into the dangerous proximity of "Our Station."

Our Stage-Coaching

The march of intellect can scarcely keep pace with the march of improvement that is manifesting itself at Kabob. To be sure, we do draw from our wells, as did our forefathers and foremothers in the days of old, in pre-Noahtic times, before the luxury of the domestic pump had been discovered, and its ingenious and costly machinery was brought home to our hearths and our yards;-to be sure, such elaborate contrivances have not yet been introduced into the sunny East;—to be sure, we have not got our iron roads, and the traveller, unless he would resign himself to be transported on bearers' shoulders ingloriously, must progress upon his expedition at the inconceivable rapidity of ten good miles diurnally. But such atrocities are no longer imperative, for the "Kabob Transit Company" has been established, and we have the glorious facility promised to us, of being able to reach the capital of Bobarchy, which is one hundred and fifty miles off, in six-and-thirty hours!!

Is not this a matter of congratulation, that the great towns of the plains of Dekchy should be thus brought into

such proximate and intimate communication with each other?
that the bonds of mutual intercourse may be so closely knit,
and the human families of the province of Bobarchy be
as one?

Kabob must be congratulated! Nor need the felicitations
end here; for, under the influence of the great McGhee, who
detected a fresh opening for a profitable investment of his
redundant wealth, started at once a rival firm, and the "Kabob
Truck Transit Company" has its dangerous competitor in the
"General Inland Tatoo Traction Company."

And now let us take our journey to the capital. We will
patronize the "Kabob Truck Transit Company," which, by its
title, provides trucks, upon which you can lash your palankeen.
The ingenuity of the device in their construction is only to be
equalled by the pertinacity of the structure, which, with all the
rude treatment it experiences, declines resolutely to fall to
pieces, although those front-springs will persist in drooping so
alarmingly. Did I say springs? — I mean plates of the rigidest
iron, which, to moderate their too great elasticity, as
communicated to us by the managing secretary, are further
rendered immovable by being girt around with thongs of
catgut and strips of the stiffest and most inflexible bamboo.

We have booked our places The Kabob post-chaise is
brought to our door—always allowing that the animal in the
shafts is disposed to accede to such an arrangement. The
truck has reached our dwelling; our palankeen is lashed
thereon; and our provender for the way (for we are mortals
of a suspicious turn of mind, and are in full assurance of some
pending calamities) is laid in to the tune of much bitter beer,
considerable sodas, and hermetically-sealed delicacies
unexpressed.

Our gateway, spacious in its width, from the circumstance
of one pillar having been annihilated by the wheels of one

Griff's dog-cart, offers no obstacle to an easy passage for our vehicle, which, through the good dispostion of the horse, and under the consideration and full expectation that he is about to return to his gram-bag, has unhesitatingly condescended to make a start. The Jehu is delighted. He clambers on his perch, handles his ribbon as he would a bunch of carrots; flourishes his long-lashed whip, with which he thwacks the dorsal vertebræ of the too generous steed until he breaks into a canter. The horse-keeper, after desperate efforts, and with much puffing, and not a little scraping of his legs on the rapidly-rotating wheel, hoists himself by the side of the charioteer, and we are fairly off.

We puff away at our cheroot, and cherish fond hopes that, as the quadruped between the shafts has evinced such serenity of disposition, our progress may not be marred by any egregious manifestation of ill will on his part, when, in the twinkling of an eye, we find ourselves shot up into the roof of our vehicle, to the scarification of our shin-bones by that detestably-protruding shelf and drawer. We descend with still greater velocity, hear a crushing of masonry, a din of voices, imprecatory and abusive in their nature. We clear our eyes from the dust that has blinded them, and discover that our steed has wilfully diverged from the appointed way, and striven to make direct for his gram, with a total disregard for drain-bridges, or any such opposive hinderances, and deposited our vehicle in the contiguous field. But we lie tranquil, and submit ourselves to the mercies of the Jehu to eradicate us from the ditch and the dilemma.

The offending quadruped, the author of all our grief, is reposing on his side; but by repeated applications of pole and thong, is restored to his legs, and a sense of his conduct. The truck is dragged on to the road, and the animal once more harnessed, and solicited to start.

But no—imprecations, objurgations, thwacks, puncturings, and poles, are resorted to in vain; our tatoo's are impervious to all. We watch the proceedings: in vain the niggers exert their utmost muscular capabilities, almost to the bursting of their livers, in striving to make the wheels revolve; in vain do they strive to propel the vehicle by applying themselves to the shafts; in vain does the lash fall heavily on the flanks, and eyes, and ears, and head of the tat; in vain does the pole alight on his ribs, or the twitch wrung round his nose excite any symptom of aught but retrogressive motion. But at last, by the ingenious device of coiling a rope round a fore-leg, and hauling at it, the tat, finding himself becoming on a more and more insecure footing, changes his tactics, springs forward, with a seeming determination to crush his tormentors, and away we go at the rate of forty miles an hour!

Then we have a repetition of the pleasing little prelude to each stage on the occasion of every change, which occurs at every five miles. But still we progress, and, through the inequalities of the road, we pass a joyful time of it, about equally divided between our mattress and the roof of our vehicle. We find our bones rather sore, and our bottles rather broken; our soda-water and our patience are exhausted; but the wheels of our truck do hold on—the Jehu does persevere—the tats of the "Truck Transit Company" do exhibit incongruous tempers, but at last we arrive, in about double the time we expected when we left "Our Station."

Our Agriculturists

We do occasionally indulge in rusticity, and partake of the pleasures of the pastoral life. From the giddy whirl of gaiety—from that vortex of dissipation in which we are eternally plunged at the delectable Kabob, we pitch our tent

> "Where stillness betokens a peaceful retreat
> In the depths of the dark forest glade!"

and away from the fascinating allurements of town life, and amid the agriculturists of Ind, devote a happy hour.

We thus indulge in rural pleasures and the produce of the gun simultaneously. The early dawn finds us in the field, not 'ramping among the turnips, but trudging about the swampy ground in search of snipe, accompanied by our dogs, which we do flatter ourselves are lineal descendants of the best blood, and of the most aristocratic of the canine species, addicted to game,—dogs superlatively handsome, with tails judiciously abridged, and ears depending exuberantly. A sable valet carries the double-barrelled gun; a second bears the powder and the shot; a third delights in conveying the needful treasure of soda and of brandy; a fourth the umbrella;—all followed by our springhtly tat, led by his sable groom.

And so we tramp about until the sun's perpendicular height illumines the depths of our skulls, when we have recourse to the saddle, and loiter listlessly on our homeward way.

Then are the table attendeants actively alert; the sacrifice of the chicken has been accomplished; the savoury condiments for our Curry have been amalgamated, and are seething in the pot; the everlasting omelette is about to be cooked, and the unfermented cakes prepared. Then we indulge in our bath, and at the door of our tent, placing ourselves in a suitable position, receive the welcome shower from the hand of the watercarrier. We reinvest our limbs in the lightest and the loosest of vestments, and then we breakfast. Fire is next vehemently called for, by which our fragrant cheroots are lit; we throw ourselves on to the cot of ease, and resign ourselves to the indulgence of the latest periodical, with occasional interpolations of the "balmy".

Thus we while away the lingering hour, till hunger and the slave warn us it is time for tiffin. The feast is spread, the pale ale glimmers in the glass; we find that the tent's high temperature, the morning walk, the mid-day slumber, have parched the throat, and that one bottle is of no avail—we try a second, and that scoundrel slave asserts we try a third. But we have had a famous dinner. The Curry, flavoured with a spicy pungency, is good indeed—the pale ale most insinuating. We once more call for fire, and then like a good old patriarch in days of yore, we sit at the door of our tent and watch the flocks and herds, and much cattle, as they "wind slowly o'er the lea," and pass our tent; and as

"The ploughman homeward plods his weary way,"

we think what a comical ploughman he is—not as you may picture to yourself, a swarthy, sun-burnt English rustic, with his team of giant horses, wending his weary way, while the plough—that ponderous implement—remains in the headland for the morrow's use; but a supple son of Ind. See, there is one: his labours for the day are o'er; the wearied bullocks, relieved from their work, steer homeward by their way. He follows, "with solemn step and slow," carrying the plough upon his head!

Then, as we sit at the door of our tent, and the evening shadows are lengthening, we watch

> "The village train, from labour free,
> Lead up their sports beneath the spreading tree."

The sable mother issues from her door, and with her offspring straddling on her hip, watches the return of her lord. The wearied mechanics sally forth, and, squatting by their huts, smoke their hubble-bubbles, and talk of pice; while the younger branches of the community, with the shrillest of voices, give themselves up unreservedly to amusement, and screechings of delight.

Then darkness falls upon the plain, and lights are burning in our tent; and as we sit without, the bats and the beetles buzz about our ear and bang into our eyes. The frogs set up their chorus, the crickets their chirrup, and the kids, abstracted from their mothers, bewail their fate with intolerable bleating. Then the head man of the village comes to pay us his respects. We give him a chair, and if our colloquial acquirements admit of the luxury, we indulge in a discourse anent the crops, the climate, and the state of things in general, and of the village in particular, until our slave announcing our evening's repast, we solicit his adjournment, and betake ourselves to dinner.

And so the lingering hours glide on, and bitter beer glides down. The smoke from the village, as the hungered rustics cooked their daily meal, and which had well-nigh suffocated us, has now cleared away. The village dog has begun to prowl about, and in his audacity has invaded our tent. But a tent-peg alighting seriously on his hips has caused him to vacate. We once more take to the easy-chair without, and gaze upon the

> "Glimmering land,
> Lit with a low large moon."

The village is hushed in silence, save by the bayings of the dogs and the faint yelpings of the jackal, which is yet afar. We begin to nod, fling ourselves upon our cot, and soon, forgetful of jackals, dogs, and villages, fall into a pleasant dream, and imagine that we are fifty thousand miles away from "Our Station."

Our Nuwab

Among the magnates of "Our Station,"—and I had almost been so unthankful as to omit him in this faithful record,—is that Oriental potentate, the Nuwab of Kabob. Imbued with much generosity, and impregnated with a taste for English sports and pastimes, the Nuwab is a character of considerable appreciation among us. Where he picked up his predilections for our race has not transpired, nor is it a matter for the display of any anxiety. Suffice it to know that the Nuwab is game for anything, from a pool of billiards to giving a ball to the Station.

That is the Nuwab's palace, if you can call that accumulation of tattered buildings of brick and mud and plaster a palace. But let us introduce you to him, let us drive up to his house. There he is, bedecked in gold-embroidered velvet, with a velvet-and-gold turban; pearls descend from his ears, and patent-leather shoes encompass his feet, which are clothed in stockings; across his shoulders is a Cashmere shawl, and he smokes his hookah, waiting till his equipage is ready.

But look at his sporting turn-out; an old English drag, imported by General Bamboo, and with which the old general "stuck" the Nuwab when he went home. And, by the way, you should examine the Palace: it is a perfect refuge for the destitute,—destitute articles, for which no purchasers could be found when their owners left Kabob, and of which the benevolent Nuwab relieved them;—articles that an unaccomplished Oriental would find great use for; such as pianos by the dozen—desperate creations, that make the tips of your fingers tingle to touch; harps, babies' cots, four-post bedsteads, ladies' wardrobes, marble-topped round tables, and the like. Then there are carriages *ad infinitum,*—veritable arks, with gigantic springs, and violently yellow in complexion; lofty mail phaetons, with hoods, once down, no power on earth could cause to be put up again; and billiard-tables, with caverns for pockets and a prevailing irregularity of surface, engendered by the curling up of the wood. But the Nuwab shrugs his shoulders, smiles, and knows full well that his asylum is stocked, not from any absolute necessity for the things that are to be found therein, but from sheer feelings of charity to relieve the oppressed of their superfluous furniture.

See, the Nuwab, who knows it is sporting to drive four-in-hand, and so thoroughly English, retains the fashion, but somewhat Orientalizes it. For, instead of handing the ribbons himself, he squats cross-legged on his velvet cushion, which spread on the roof, and there, while his Jehu,

> "With whistling thong,
> Urges at speed his pranching team along,"

the Nuwab puffs away at his hookah; occasionally roused, however, by the urgent necessity that frequently arises of having to hold on tight, as the team, taking the Jehu where they like, whirls suddenly round some sharp turning. But note the putting-to; would it not convulse a genuine English Jarvie to behold? First the Jehu gains his seat, next come the leaders, who are duly installed, and their reins unite them to the whip; then are the wheelers brought to the scratch, and with much rearing and plunging, much lying down on the pole and other extravagant physical contortions, the steeds are announced to be ready. The Nuwab surmounts the roof by means of a ladder; he crosses his legs; the reins have entangled themselves in the Jehu's palm; the horse-keepers suspend their chirrupings and remonstrances; the near leader, a ginger-coloured brute with a stiltish style of leg, and the off wheeler, a cream-colour with the pinkest of eyes, stand on their respective hind legs, receive the maledictions and the cudgellings of the bystanders, spring forward, and away they all go.

With this equipage our Nuwab occasionally comes to the Band, where he dismounts and talks to the ladies, whom he invites to a nautch at his own mansion.

And now, let us drop in to his palace on such an occasion. The guests arrive, and are installed in velvet-cushioned chairs, and otto of roses is handed round, with dried fruits and sweetmeats. Then come the dancing-girls, gyrating on their heels, ogling and leering, and shaking their uplifted palms, with other idiotic contortions, indicative, in the Eastern eye, of grace and dignity of motion. But "Our Nuwab" invites us to supper and there we find tables groaning with productions of Sticker Doss's Europe shop, for which "Our Nuwab" has given unlimited orders. But liberality and redundancy have been more considered than appropriateness of assortment. Lobsters and "tart fruits" commingle, while truffled sausages and sugared almonds share mutually the same dish. Nor is it for want of crockery, as dishes and plates, and vessels even of the most domestic character, grace the board, side by side with silver plate and glittering ormoulu, to the unsmotherable amusement of the guests.

But the wines and beer have been properly cooled, and considering they came from Sticker Doss's, are not so bad. We have great fun, and the laughter is prodigious. The Nuwab, who, as a strict Hindoo, sits complacently a looker-on, joining in our mirth, but urging us to partake with greater courage, which, indeed, it needs, for the table slaves of his highness are not adepts at Christian cookery, and trifling irregularities greet the senses. The salad indicates the presence of cod-liver oil, and we have faint suspicious that "Day & Martin" has been introduced as a sauce.

But the Nuwab is in blissful unconsciousness of it all, and we drink to his health in three times three, which gratifies him intensely. Then we adjourn to witness the fireworks, and a troop of fifty pariah-dogs let loose, each with a lighted squib at his tail, is pronounced to be great sport. The Nuwab is pleasantness itself. He offers the loan of his elephants at any time, and hopes we will join him on his next shooting expedition; promises to show us his new rifle, which his old friend Bamboo has sent him as a present from England; and then, with a cordial shake of the hand, he wishes us good night, and expresses (in Hindustani, for he cannot speak English) a hope that he may often be gratified by having the happiness of affording such gaiety as is in his power to the residents of "Our Station."

OUR NUWAB Page No. 109

OUR THEATRICALS Page No. 113

OUR BAZAR Page No. 11

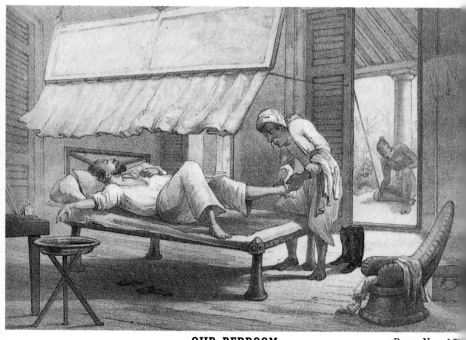

OUR BEDROOM Page No. 12

Our Theatricals

Of course we have private theatricals, — the gallant votaries of Thespis get up for the amusement of delighted audiences melodramas of the most absorbing interest, and farces intensely facetious.

One end of the assembly-room is set apart for a stage, the floor of the centre is removed for the occasion, and this hold, as it were, forms the pit and orchestra. The stage is a fixture, and the ingenuity displayed in making the most of a very circumscribed sphere of action is a matter for admiration. The side scenes are but three, and are on triangular frames, which revolve. One side exhibits nature in its wild flowers of the forest. Turn the scene, and you are plunged at once into the retirement of domestic and civilized life — a book-shelf in a *négligé* state, and the portrait of a flaxen-headed cowboy, doing something o'er the lea, arrest the attention of the admiring spectator; and thirdly, masses of brown ochre are designed to represent rocks or whatever fancy may suggest. The back scenes are a corresponding trio, that roll up — one a wood for the romantic and the perpetration of horrible murders, with a circular cut in a dab of sky for the addition of a gentle moon when requisite. Then we have an interior, which, by a judicious arrangement of properties, duly set in order by the momentary introduction of a John, whose livery consists of a strip of yellow paper tacked to his collar and cuffs, can equally represent the boudoir for interviews with unfavouring papas, or the drawing-room, where scenes in connection with bended knees are commonly enacted; as, by the addition of a couch with a sheet thrown over a stick, it will form a bedroom. Lastly, we have a dungeon, for the express benefit of enchained gentlemen who have got solos to communicate. Great, however, as is the artistic excellence of these scenes, the drop is incomparably superb. Some ambitious individual, overflowing with perspective on a novel system, has poured it forth on canvas in the shape of columns ingeniously receding to the front and approaching to the rear.

But to the play. Let us pop behind the scenes. The band has thundered forth its operatic airs; the company have poured in; the melodramatizers, after a world of commotion and a profusion of scuffling and driving off of servants, have at last fairly commenced operations; the bell has tinkled; the prompter has hauled up the green curtain, to the detriment of his tights and the discomposure of his temper; the drama has opened-touching are the scenes-unnerved are the spectators-pocket-handkerchiefs are in demand; the plot thickens-the climax is at hand. Chumuch is the hero; a touching scene lies before him; he is in difficulties—he hums—he haws—he edges off to the wings—he eyes the prompter imploringly.

"Weep," whispers the prompter, compassionately.

"What? What?"

"Weep! wee-ep! wee-e-ep;" speaks the prompter, in a graduated crescendo scale.

"What? — What the deuce is it? Speak out!"

"Weep!" shouts the prompter. "Confound it; can't you weep? — Weep!" roars the prompter.

The touching appeal, together with the emphatic reply, has caught the ear of the house, and the laughter is prodigious; but Chumuch, unabashed, faces the storm, and weeps convulsively.

The drama is concluded. Now let us hear Blades sing his comic song. Blades is our serjeant-major, was an undertaker before he enlisted, is an excellent actor of low life, with a fund of original humour. We couldn't do without Blades, for he fills up rejected parts that our leading Thespians would scorn to accept. But somehow or other Blades makes his few sentences tell with greater effect than all the rest of the performances, for he is such a wag, and plays so well. To be sure he "exasperates" his h's, and is apt to hear "futsteps a comin'," when he will be hoff to claim the "hands of his Hevelina for his bride;" but he is a thorough good mimic for all that.

And now let us watch the preparations for the farce. Motey is to personate Julia, and he is now undergoing the operation of having his waist clewed in by Hawser, the Prussian soldier, who is sedulously engaged in the domestic duties of a lady's-maid. Muggins is learning his part; while Mirrich, skilled in face-painting, operates upon the whole *corps dramatique*. A paper of rouge, a box of violet-powder, and a burnt cork compose his materials. Nor is his office a sinecure, as, with a thermometer at 96°, and not a breath of air, periodical repairs are many and oft. Well — the farce begins; the prompter, that most important functionary, renders salutary assistance. For my part, I rather envy the prompter: Chumuch and others vow he won't speak loud enough, while Muggins and the rest declare that he always shoves in his oar when not wanted, so that his office must be a highly desirable one. However, the play is over, loud are the plaudits, delighted are the audience, pleased but uncomfortably hot are the actors.

There is a supper at the mess for the *corps dramatique* and numerous friends, including the ladies. The health of the actors is proposed; our manager says something funny; the play is discussed; loud is the laughter, merry are the company; and before they separate it is fully decided that another performance, on some very early occasion, shall come off to enliven the community of "Our Station."

Our Bazar

At the eastern side of Kabob are the habitations devoted to the native population—constructions of mud that frown grimly at each other across the narrow, dirty ways that separate them, and which form the thoroughfares that intersect, bisect, and dissect the Great Bazar of Kabob. The dwellings, in their prevailing feature, combine the attractiveness of the primitive mound of earth with the characteristics of the pigsty. They form blocks of mud, perforated with apertures of very limited dimensions. But there are grand exceptions, for the Great Bazar can boast of at least three mansions, double in their stories, and the amount of brick-coloured paint which adorns their *façades*, in the shape of hideous demons and still more hideous animals, inexplicable in their anatomy, together with portraitures of celebrated Eastern kings, with the very yellowest of complexions and the very widest-opened eyes, would strike admiration into the heart of every beholder. And then the upper stories, with their gorgeous balconies, at least fourteen inches wide, with daintily-carved parapets a good seven inches

high, and painted every colour under the sun, shed an air of
aristocratic splendour around. These are the palaces of the
nobles. There, in that one, more splendid than its fellows,
dwells Chouse Lall; and here, in this one opposite, resides
Bunya Doss, the great contractor, of the grain caste. There,
below, in the open shop, reposing on their hams, and smoking
their hubble-bubbles, are his assistants, dispensing grain of
every kind to the tempted passer-by; and there, in front,
stands a buffalo, sniffing the good things which the uncouth
monster has already grabbed at on his way, and for which his
dense hide has been punctured accordingly. Opposite is a
confectioner's shop; to be sure we miss the ice-creams and
tartlets, the jellies, and the bath-bun and plum, the pastry and
the cakes. But do we not see, and do not our mouths water at
the contents of those brazen dishes, those savoury-looking
mounds of tawny-coloured sweetmeats—combinations of oil,
of treacle, and of flour, upon which the eyes of those two
urchins have fallen and are feasting; and in which the Oriental
damsel, with coin at command, is about to invest, lured by
that pungent odour which, penetrating our olfactories, reaches
to the very roots of our hair?

But let us pass on, if that gaunt, half-famished hound, all
covered with sores—a very Lazarus of dogs—will but gratify
our wishes by making way, and adjourning with his bone to
some more convenient locality. There goes a native, carrying
his bed and walking; and in that you see how such a
performance was enacted some eighteen hundred years ago,
when those miraculously cured of their diseases took up their
beds and walked—not, you perceive, as the imaginative artists
of the West love to portray such scenes, by depicting weak
men staggering along under huge and highly-carved
fourposters; for, you observe that eight short sticks and a few
yards of string are all that composes an Oriental's bed. And

this act of taking up his bed and walking is the commonest object in an Eastern city that falls upon the eye. There goes a woman with her pitcher of water from the well, bearing it so dexterously on her head,—a performance by which the daughters of the East acquire that uprightness of form which particularly characterizes them, and which consequently imparts to them their greatest attraction.

But let us get away from this din. That fellow who is about to feed, and who is blowing so desperately into that confounded horn, is driving the Devil away—quite enough to do it, I should imagine. This is the Hindoo temple, and this violent ringing of bells and banging of gongs would, I suspect, have a similar effect of driving away their gods.

Take care, or that Brahminee bull will have his horns into your ribs. Look at the bloated beast,—he is holy, and the Hindoos rever him. He is let loose in the streets, and is fed till, as you see, he can scarcely walk, save to reach the grain merchant's open store, and help himself at his will. Capital practice for our Griffs are these bulls: to shoot one openly would be to create an uproar in the city; but great sport they afford, and bullets go plump into their fat sides with a sound delicious to the ear. See, there goes one limping along. I shrewdly suspect a rifle-ball has very accidentally struck that joint, and that rifle the property of some Griff. We sometimes entice them to our gardens, and teach them the art of drawing water from our wells, at which we find they are great adepts, and to which the Hindoos do not object, as it saves their pockets, and their religion is not affected, as the animals are not injured. But if the Hindoos are glad to be absolved from having to feed them, the public at large are only too rejoiced to get rid of what is universally considered to be a nuisance to "Our Station."

Our Bed Room

"Sahib!—Sahib!—Sahib!"—and so it goes on, that voice of the valet, gradually increasing in force and earnestness of appeal. Firstly, of a mild and indicative tone; then explicative,—remonstrative,-until it becomes imperative and decisive and the slumberer is roused to a full comprehension of the fact that the gun has fired,—that it is daybreak—that it is getting late—that the horse is ready—that it is parade-time; that, in fact, it is contrary to right, reason, and reputation, to lie any longer a courtier of repose. But we are not to be defrauded of our utmost limits of rest: the night has been a stifling one; we have been lying simmering on our cot, gasping as we gazed at the superpending punkah, which waved listlessly to and fro, producing but a slight motion of the air; we watched its irregular style of proceeding with increasing dissatisfaction and perspiration; we observed that its speed was gradually getting

"Small by degrees and beautifully less,"

until its motion died away; when the suddenly startled native, aroused to a sense of his sleepiness and the loss of his rope, would seize it afresh and pull as if to tear it down. Then we watched again, and coveted the sleep that would befall our coolie's eyelids and spurned to court our own. The punkah-wind lulled, and the flounce was hushed into repose: we knew it well,—that brute, that pagan, had succumbed again into the arms of the sleepy god, and we lay there bathed in perspiration, and awake. A boot,—two boots,—a slipper,—two slippers, did we expend in vain as missiles, projected with unerring precision at his head. We tried a chair; but no, the vile heathen was impervious even to that; until a personal assault, effected to the detriment of our feet in kneading the outcast's ribs, did at last restore him from oblivion to his rope.

Then would we simmer again, and long for sleep. We would listen to the sharp buzz of the mosquitoes, which, driven away by the punkah, held their concert by the ceiling and in the adjoining rooms. We hear the loud croakings of the loquacious frog outside, the shrill and never-ceasing chirrup of the crickets that infest every crevice of the house within. We watch a musk-rat, which we discover it to be from its odour, on its midnight rounds. We let fly one of our recovered slipppers at it, but without effect. We feel something cold and slimy on our forehead, and knocking it off, find it to have been a lizard. And then the stoppage of the punkah necessitates a second excursion into the verandah to puncture the head of the coolie, for which, on this occasion, we employ a foreign substance in the form of a racket-bat, in lieu of our digits or our toes, and with great effect. And then we try to sleep again. We drink up all the water in the room. We shout, and the supplementary and relieving coolie wakes up our valet, who is snoring profusely in the other verandah. He brings us soda and brandy. And then we simmer again, and, accidentally, sleep does come and alight upon our exhausted frame, just as the big gun booms in the distance, and our ears are saluted with the "Sahib! Sahib!" that announces it is the hour to get up.

And then we dream we are in a land of luxury and of ease, reposing on a soft couch in some lovely spot, where

> "Every air is heavy with the sighs
> Of orange groves, and music from sweet lutes,
> And murmurs of low fountains, that gush forth
> I' the midst of roses!"

When "Sahib! — Sahib!" falls reiterated on the ear and transports us from the land of dreams to the mat-covered cot of our stifling bungalow.

But we dose on, and our valet puts on our socks, and our boots, and our pantaloons, brings the bowl — the brazen bowl — on its tripod, reiterates his solemn remonstrances that we shall be late — helps us to accomplish the formidable operation of the toilette, which the languid frame is too loath to perform.

Then as we put on the upper garments and sally forth, our table slave brings us our morning cup of tea, which, hot as it is, is refreshing to our parched throat on this sultry morning. We light our cheroot, and mount our steed; while the hosekeeper, charged with the safety and the carrying of our sword (which is an implement of far too ponderous a nature for exhausted humanity to convey beyond what dire necessity requires) scampers away to the Parade, and we follow.

"Our Bed Room," you must acknowledge, is not over-crowded with upholstery: the cot (defrauded of its mattress, but with a strip of fine matting in its stead), a table, chair, and bowl, are all that it can boast of. We do at times desert its floor, and take our cot and stretch ourselves with the stars for our canopy and the fresh breath of heaven for our punkah, when there is any; but our predilections do not run in favour

of snakes, and scorpions, and centipedes, and prowling
ravenous dogs that carry on contention by our side, nor
jackals that come howling in our ears, which, acting in
combination with a temperature at 100°, is anything but
provocative of sleep: so we retreat once more to our chamber,
to welcome even the little air that a considerate coolie will be
inclined to give, and the comparative coolness it affords.

A night in the hot season, I think you will agree with me,
is not calculated to impress you with a desire to become a
sojourner of "Our station."

Our Travellers Bungalow

The weather is hot—hot decidedly—a residence in a frying-pan, on a blazing English kitchen fire, is Paradise to it. The night, too, is sultry; the darkness has not mitigated the fury of the blast. We gasp in our palankeens, we take long pulls and strong pulls at our insinuating bottles, and startle the niggers at the perpetual poppings of the soda-water corks, that keep up a heavy file-fire throughout the night. As day dawns, we struggle with somnolency till the sun rises, and darts its downward rays into our cramped abode with intolerable intensity. We begin to be somewhat weary of this Indian night's entertainment, and have a mighty craving for a cup of hot tea or coffee, and a longing desire to expurgate from our eyes, and ears, and hair, the dust that has invaded them.

But the fates forbid it. The panting bearer, as he patters alongside, announces with grim satisfaction that we are *"very near,"* which, on the institution of a rigorous cross-questioning, resolves itself into the awful fact that we have still ten miles before us. And as the sun has "scaled the vaulted skies," and in its course has already split the top of our gun-case, and curled up the lid of our cheroot-box, and the prospect of our own vile body being frizzled by its penetrative rays is more than a possible contingency, the hope deferred makes our hearts more than sick.

But here we are at last, thank Heaven! — at the "Travellers' Bungalow." We extricate ourselves from the palankeen, which is borne into the verandah, and our immediate wants are instantly the source of anxious solicitude on the part of the "sweetly smiling, sweetly talking" slaves. That venerable patriarch of self-complacent mien is the purveyor of the institution, and with unbounded largeness of views, and a broad idea of his own capabilities and the expansiveness of the larder, interrogates us as to our requirements, which he can meet to any extent. He is prepared to supply us with the most dainty food in endless variety, if we will but express our sentiments and expound our views. Hot rolls and buttered toast, cold ham and sausages, raised pie, and other delicacies, float before our imagination. But the horrid heathen, the vile pagan, destroys our dream of hope. His expressions prove to be of the metaphorical order, and we discover that hot water for our tea, a grilled fowl, and an unfermented cake, are "all the store that he can give to me."

We resign ourselves to this reduced state of things; and while the second slave is providing water for our ablution, we unfold our thoughts, and our dressing-case-when lo! a rush is heard in the verandah, a noise of many footsteps, and a chuckling as of domestic poultry, when, fast pursued by the venerable patriarch intent on slaughter and our breakfast — a cock — a weather-beaten cock, —

"A gallant cock
As ever roused the echoes of the morn,

> And from his stately dunghill throne
> Crow'd lustily,"—

a cock more patriarchal than its lord—invades our presence, with conscious certainty that his broad sinewy frame is doomed to grace our board. Aroused to his danger by the flight of a projectile which nears his head, he flees away. Incited by the love of sport, we join the chase. Away we go, the gallant cock making for the kitchen; when a stout stick impelled by the hand of the supplementary slave diverts his course of flight, but impinges on the sharp joints of a half-famished dog that prowls about for food, which limps away howling in his anguish. Away goes the cock. Lengthy in leg, he strides across the plain, periodically the object of a brickbat and a slipper. Now he makes for the verandah, when a second dog, excited to pursue, contributes his quota of assistance, until the game, disquieted by the flight of missiles, once more seeks the refuge of our chamber, when the artful projection of a slipper knocks him into the hands of his slayer.

We perform our ablutions, we reinvest ourselves in garments of the airiest texture, when breakfast is declared, and there the once gallant cock, so late the object of our pursuit, lies recumbent on the dish, like an uncomfortably flattened frog.

With all the ardour of our being, with all the muscular development of our lower jaw, we strive to masticate the obdurate bird; but no—its flesh is impervious to the sharpest incisor, and spurns the efforts of the most crushing molar, and we rest satisfied with the assurance that we are tackling the identical cock that came out of the Ark. But the hot tea, which we have made from our own supply, refreshes us; and with the other accessories obtained from that same store— our palankeen—we refresh the inner man.

The sable patriarch offers to immolate a second fowl for our early dinner; but we decline the proffered sacrifice, as our morning's experience of the dish, popularly called "a sudden death," does not warrant our indulging in a repetition of the luxury; so we dine off the contents of a hermetically-sealed tin of more savoury food.

The hours lag long and wearily. The punkah, of limited dimensions, with a deranged flounce and with unsymmetrical ropes, waggles with a quaint and threatening aspect, and affords but little mitigation of the burning heat. We have a tattie at the door, and the slave keeps it well saturated but its ambiguous form admits the fiery blast. We lie recumbent on the cot, which has the authorized and popular number of legs, of which the chairs cannot be said to boast; we have dozed; we have read the regulations that hang upon the walls forty times at least, till we know them by heart; we have drunk tepid beer, and warm soda-water has allayed our thirst; we have recorded our names in the book of fate and of the Bungalow; when, at last, upon a grateful ear the sounds of the relieving palankeen-bearers announce that the sun has set and that the hour of departure is at hand.

The palankeen is once more furnished with our goods, the tax for the shelter is paid. The grinning attendant, implicitly believing in his inmost soul that he has afforded us the most unqualified satisfaction, receives a donation with a smile of happy contentment. We light our cheroot, struggle into our palankeen, and, amidst the grateful salaamings of the˙niggers, start again upon our journey, and trust that before daylight we shall arrive once more at "Our Station."

Our Cook Room

$\mathcal{I}$s there not a luxury in the very contemplation of a kitchen,—as the fragrant smells of savoury good things insinuate themselves up the stairs, and through the crevices of the doors, arrest the senses, and whet the appetite? And is it not refreshing to the eye to explore the arcana of a cook's laboratory—to see the glittering array of saucepans, the rows of cleanest crockery marshalled on their shelves, the cups and jugs hung pendent from the ledge, the table and the dresser with their spotless purity; and then the glittering range, with the bright fire blazing in the grate, and all the appurtenances and appliances arranged in the neatest order and precision, while cleanliness is the conspicuous feature in it all? We see before us the delicious joint, revolving on its spit; and the presiding genius of the scene, with blooming face, though somewhat scorched, and brawny arms, wielding the basting-spoon, and skilfully handling it, while the rich gravy rolls its savoury course upon the bright joint that is gradually browning to perfection. And then to see the mincing, and the chopping, and all the little delicate manipulations in

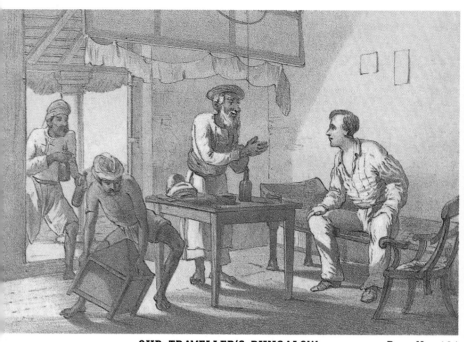

OUR TRAVELLER'S BUNGALOW   Page No. 124

OUR COOK ROOM   Page No. 128

OUR CLOTH MERCHANTS

Page No. 13

OUR PIG STICKING

Page No. 1

the concoction of nice things, so artfully executed on the dresser.

Do we, in our exile, have all these things? Are our cooks plump, and red-faced, and brawny? Are our kitchens the scenes of spotless purity, and our grates radiant with the gleam of the blazing coal? Are our dishes and our cups ranged with symmetrical exactitude? and is uniformity and precision the characteristic of our culinary arrangements? I trow not—I rather think not.

Look into Oriental kitchen. If your eyes are not instantly blinded with the smoke, and if your sight can penetrate into the darkness, enter that hovel, and witness the preparation of your dinner. The table and the dresser, you observe, are Mother Earth; for niggers—Orientals, I mean—have that peculiar faculty which characterizes the ape and the kangaroo: they can only stand erect on an occasion. Let a nigger alone, and down he drops upon his hams spontaneously, with as much joy as the wretched monkey in our streets when his polka is accomplished.

The preparation for your dinner must therefore be performed in the earth's broad lap, like everything else in this Eastern land. As a matter of course, you will have Curry, the standing dish of the East. There are the slaves busy at its preparation. The chase for the fowls has terminated in a speedy capture. Already the feathers are being stripped, and the mixture of the spicy condiments is in course of preparation. There, on his hams, is the attractive-looking assistant, grinding away the savoury stuff which is soon to adorn that scraggy chicken, and to excite the palling appetite. There is the prime mover of the undertaking, trimming with a skilful hand the other domestic fowl, that has been immolated for cutlets. And a not over-alluring object is that head of the culinary department, I must confess—a venerable man with silvery locks. We entertain the most profound respect for grey hairs, but only when in their legitimate sphere of utility. They grace the head of the aged; but there is an insecurity respecting them which in our humble view militates against the desirability of an ancient cook.

> "Man wants but little *hair* below,
> Nor wants that little long."

And when we see the snowy locks that flutter in the breeze, we sincerely trust that they will continue to flutter in the breeze, and not invade the sanctity of the saucepan.

Observe the kitchen-range, I beseech you: a mud construction, with apertures for the reception of charcoal, upon which repose pans of native mould, in which the delicacies are cooked. And as for the roasting! Yes—there is a spit; but the only smoke-jack is the smoke-begrimed nigger, who, reposing on his hams, turns the implement himself, which stretches across some lighted charcoal on the ground.

Thus, you perceive, simplicity is the prevailing feature in an Indian kitchen. A spit, two native saucepans, a ladle, and a knife, comprise all the requiements of an Eastern cook. His grate is extemporized at a moment's warning with a lump of mud and a cruse of water. And if the cooks of the West have more costly and more extensive appliances, and laugh to scorn the rude apparatus of the Eastern Soyers, let them laugh triumphantly when they show that, even with their perfect means, they can turn out a better dinner, which we doubt. If the native heeds not the smoke, if he prefers the ground to a table, and rude implements used in a primitive fashion, he can and does, with equal facility, dress a dinner in the tented field, under the canopy of heaven's blue vault, as in his cooking-room at home, with an aptitude and a skill that gladdens the heart of the epicure on his march, and affords to the traveller, when far removed from the busy haunts of men, the certainty of as excellent a dinner as ever graced his table in the land of the West.

The aspect of the Eastern kitchen is not inviting, nor are its inmates, in their outer man, objects of alluring attractiveness. But sit you at your mahogany, and taste the labour of their hands, and whoever questions that dishes delicious and mouth-watering can be dressed by an Eastern cook, let him come at once to Kabob, and we will prove to him what really good things can be got at "Our Station."

Our Cloth Merchants

*K*abob is proud of its Merchants; their energies are exhaustless, their credit unfathomable, and their wealth unbounded. If they have not ships bounding across the wide ocean, freighted with their stores—if they have not correspondents and associates in every land—if they have not shops which display in rich profusion the measure of their wealth—and if they have not their rural seats where they can rub off the pen-and-ink, the brown-paper-parcel proceedings of the day,—they have their ships of the desert-they have their creaking carts, bounding over the rugged roads of neighbouring provinces, ponderous with the bales of treasure that they love to barter for the rupees of our community, which flow into their coffers. They have the very soul of profit within them their dwellings are in the lordliest hovels of our city; their bundles traverse every street, and their bills haunt every bungalow.

Would you seek the possession of what they have to dispose of? You need not order your carriage and drive to the fashionable shop; you will find no counter, backed by simpering slaves, seductive in their insinuating offers, and smiling with self-complacency. The Merchants of Kabob are of the peripatetic school. Their shops are, figuratively, on their heads; and their worldly goods are brought into your immediate presence before your wants and desires are even divulged. I really do not know what the ladies of Kabob, and of India in general, would do—how they could possibly

"Lure the lingering hours along,"

were it not for the itinerant Merchants, those sons of the pack and the yard, of the linen, the velvet, and the silk. They are the safety-valves for England's daughters, which allow of the escape of that tedium and apathetic indolence which would otherwise destroy the vital spark. It is a striking fact, which has hitherto escaped the eye of general observation, and which is deserving of a thorough recognition, that the introduction of a Cloth Merchant into the presence of the fair operates more successfully in restoring life and animation to the fast-fading patient than all the medicines and ministrations of the faculty. And, more than this, those fair ones who indulge in the habit of a perpetual *koprawalah* in the verandah are the liveliest and healthiest of their race. Look at Mrs. Capsicum, observe Mrs. McGhee, think of Mrs. Geedur, Mrs. Gander, and others,-how energetic, how lively, how active they one and all are. And how is this to be accounted for, but by the indisputable fact of the all-prevailing presence of the men of muslins, of ribbons, and of wools? Talk of homœopathy, of hydropathy,—give me koprawalopathy as a certain and most efficacious system for the ailments of the female portion of our Indian community.

Just step in to call on Mrs. Cardamom; she has lately become a convert to the system, and, take my word for it, you will find her drawing-room carpet

"With native plants enamelled o'er,"—

or, rather, natives' goods. There, you see, are rival Merchants, bidding for the honour of her purchase. Chouse Lall is so insinuating, and Rupee Doss is so seductive, and his goods are all so fresh—declared to be just received, and only extracted that morning from the newly-arrived bales, and never before exhibited to mortal eye in Kabob—which, between ourselves, is a declaration slightly figurative and Oriental, as we saw the rascal showing those very identical things to Mrs. Capsicum, not an hour ago. But Mrs. Cardamom thinks that tarlatan so sweet, and that ribbon so lovely, and that pair of gloves so charming; and Cardamom lets her get what she wishes, and likes to see her well dressed; and so she wavers in her previously-expressed declaration, that she would positively buy nothing. Then Chouse Lall produces the identical kind of goods, and the rivalry becomes vigorous and keen, until indignation fires the soul of Chouse Lall, and he animadverts upon the private life and character of Rupee Doss, whose black and boiling blood declines to recognize such uncalled-for reflections, retaliates with compound interest, and with comprehensive gesticulations and significant remarks of withering scorn and defiance.

The recriminations ensue, and the rivals unite in concert of vituperative melody, to the enlivenment of Mrs. Cardamom; and the final adjudication of the case by the dress-piece being obtained from Chouse Lall at one quarter of its originally-expressed value, the shutting up in desperation by Rupee Doss of his bundles, and the eventual clearing of the room; when the spark of contention once more blazes into flame in the verandah; and when this has subsided, a fresh bone of contention arises in the matter of the coin mulcted from Chouse Lall by Mrs. Cardamom's slave, who, in the payment of the wealthy merchant, has subtracted from his rightful claim the sum of one-fiftieth part of a farthing, but for which Chouse Lall battles with vehemence of manner and vigour of articulation, as if the fate of his house hinged on the result.

A valuable institution, then, is the Merchant system of Kabob. And what if the produce of their bundle is not always of the newest?—and what if the sum taken for each article is the price demanded divided by six, reduced further by a subsequent subtraction? Why, we are all similarly circumstanced, and are all at the mercy of these sable vendors, who, most unquestionably, with all their faults, are indispensable for the comfort—yes, and for the amusement and enlivenment of "Our Station."

Our Pig-Sticking

Amongst the diversity of sports, pastimes, pleasures, amusements, recreations, and the other multiplicity of enjoyments, by which we speed the loitering hours at Kabob, and enliven the intervals of parades, treasure-escorts, guard-visiting, and other such delectable avocations of a martial nature, we sally forth at times to do battle with the savage beasts of the field, and exercise our faculties of destructiveness in the annihilation of the wild boar in his jungle. But we do not patronize all the paraphernalia that distinguish this sport in the lands of the West: we have not the brazen horn,

> "With penetrating sound
> Its thrilling tones the echoing woods resound."

Nor do we need the pack of dogs to tackle our prey. The steed and the spear are all our requirements, combined, I may add, with dexterity in the use of the latter, and a capability of sticking to the saddle of the former. Dhalbhat is our most accomplished pig-sticker, and polishes off his grunter with a scientific insinuation of the spearhead into its flanks that is delightful to behold. But Dhalbhat is a clipping rider, and his Arabs are first-rate,—as active as if they were stuffed with quicksilver, and never flinching from the attack of the irascible boar, when, as in his wrath he frequently does, he wheels suddenly round and becomes the aggresor. In such moments I recommend you to exercise considerable adhesiveness to the pig-skin beneath you, or there is a contingency that may possibly arise, of the tusks of the infuriated monster being implanted in your own ribs.

But let us join Dhalbhat in his morning excursion. The tents are pitched at a village some twenty miles off; for within the neighbourhood of Kabob not a grunter can dare to show the light of his countenance. We ride over in the evening, and have our dinner on the jungle's edge, when, with "nut-brown draughts inspired," we narrate the feats of sport gone by, and talk of the coming fray.

The morning dawns. There is our sporting Griff already in his tops, and on his steed, the little Tantrums, which has become a most inveterate pig-sticker. There is Dhalbhat on a high-caste Arab, that walks with head and tail erect, in all the conscious dignity of aristocratic perfection. There is Byle on a "Waler," that is, a horse from New South Wales— for Byle is a heavy man, and the Arabs feel his weight; there is Huldey on his Cape; and, to complete the variety, there goes Topey, on an imported English mare, which has won many a race, and, though "rather groggy at the fore," has plenty of go in her still; and, lastly, there is a Griff on a genuine Hindoo,—a regular neighing, rearing, pink-eyed monster, with white nose and legs, and an amazing exuberance of spavin.

The pigs are pronounced to be plentiful; and, though the jungle is tolerably dense, there are breaks which may afford

many a good spurt, and be the scenes of many an obstinate
encounter.

We dispose ourselves in squads, and divide the field; a
few sables enlisted in our cause beat the jungle. We have not
gone far, when the pink-eyed Hindoo is seen dashing off with
his rider, who, with his young blood boiling with excitement
and anxiety to flesh his untried spear, has descried something
of the swinish form sloping away from a field. Away goes
pink-eyed Hindoo, and away goes his rider with him, into the
jungle. We follow, but are soon met by the elated Griff on his
now foaming steed, who, with triumphant energy of action,
points to his spear trickling with gore. He has done the
deed—he has killed his pig—he is a hero. Then we press on to
view the object of his triumph; which proves, however, to be
a lady pig, who, with maternal solicitude, stood by her youthful
progeny; and from which circumstance he was enabled to
accomplish the slaughter of what, in his verdancy, he believed
to be the consummation of the pig-sticker's hopes and the
acme of glory. Unmitigated chaff ruthlessly annihilates the
Griff's delight, and he and the pink-eyed Hindoo subside to
the tear.

But a regular grunter is hurried from his lair, and makes
away for an adjoining copse. Swift as the arrow from the bow
flies the Arab to cut him off. Away goes Topey, handling his
spear, on slaughter bent. The pig makes a turn upon the
Arab, which, nimble as a goat, bounds aside, and escapes the
impending tusk, while Dhalbhat, from the sudden swerve, is
only able to prick with his spear the now enraged animal,
which makes a vigorous assault upon the advancing English
mare, who, less active than the Arab, swerves aside, and
escapes the Scylla of the boar to roll over on the Charybdis of
a protruding stump, that brings her and her rider to the
ground. But Dhalbhat comes to the rescue and the pig,

backing into a dense clump, stands for a while at bay. By this time Topey has remounted. With a threatening move to the rear, the pig bethinks himself of a neighbouring ravine, and makes away for it at his utmost speed, and a speed that keeps the Arab at full gallop, I can tell you. Slap through many a brake and many a brier over the rugged ground, at racing pace, the mare at times ahead, with Topey ready for revenge. Then, by a change of course, Dhalbhat closes upon his flanks — the pace is killing—the ravine all but attained, when by a touch of the spur, and a judicious handling of the rein, Dhalbhat is able—and all in the twinkling of an eye-to plunge his spear into the heart of the great brute, which rolls lifeless into the ravine below.

Thus we carry on the game. We polish off a few more pigs, return to our tents to seek shelter in the heat of the day, and refresh ourselves. Then we gallop back into cantonments, satisfied with our morning's sport, and exciting the envy of all the sportsmen who could not join the excursion, and who, by the way, are pretty numerous at "Our Station."

Our Garden

Kabob is not be surpassed by any station in the province of Bobarchy for the beauty and the luxuriance of its gardens. Horticulture flourishes and abounds. It is true that at certain seasons of the year, when the sun is ultrapotential, there is as much vegetation in the majority of our gardens as there is on the back of a codfish; yet when the floodgates of the heavens are opened, and sheets of water have rested for a while on the face of Kabob, then to see the luxuriance of vegetation, to mark how the sandy plain is a very incarnation of verdure, would indeed gladden your eye and delight the sense.

But we have bright spots at Kabob, genuine oases in the desert, where greenness is ever to be found, where the wearied traveller may repose, if he likes it, by the crystal stream that is ever welling forth to fertilize and to refresh.

Such is "Our Garden," which affords grateful sensations to the eye, and delightful dispensations for the table, presided over by the most experienced of gardeners, a venerable man, grown gray in the cultivation of Flora, and the sterner but

more laudable procreation of the vegetable kingdom. Come
and let us walk in "Our Garden,"

"Where whispers the beech, and where
murmurs the rill,"

and watch the men of spade at work. Look at that Oriental in
the snowy vest and ample lower draperies. He is the presiding
genius of the spot. And of the "mollies and dollies" you have
heard of, he is pleased to represent the molly, while the
basket of produce he carries in his hand is the veritable dolly.
This dolly (which our Moonshee, who is dreadfully particular,
desires we should call "dhallee," as molly "mhallee") is the
combined contribution of the several beds of "Our Garden,"
which matutinally yield of their store for the master's table.
Our venerable molly (we are resolute, and persist in our
orthographical views) takes his morning rounds, culling the
fairest and the best; and then, arranging his dolly with critical
acumen and the very consummation to good taste, does he
with great solemnity, and with the smile of self-satisfied
approval lurking about the corners of his ancient mouth,
invade our presence at the breakfast-table, and offer his
vegetable oblation.

See him now laying in his stock for the morning's
presentation. His invaluable assistant—that individual whose
dress exhibits facilities for a rapid toilette—is seconding him
in his labours, and is extracting from the ground some
succulent root, which the ingenious disposition of his body
renders him capable of quickly performing. But in that elegant
and striking attitude are all the laborious operations of the
garden effected. "Blackey" *must* be ape-like, "it is his nature
too" and whether to dig, to rake, to drill, to plant, to sow,
Blackey must repose on his hams.

But let us travel on. Should you wish to study the science of irrigation, that venerable functionary will impart to you considerable knowledge. You observe that in the East the beds are on a lower level than the walks. Look at those various beds. Here are some covered with a sheet of water; there are others which have enjoyed the fructifying influence of the submersion, and are fast absorbing the liquid that was bestowed upon them; here are others which, by their parched looks, are evidently in need of, and are to be the immediate recipients of the same watery benefaction. And see how Blackey (on his hams again) distributes the supply by his skilful opening and closing of those microscopic sluicegates made of clay. And mark the source of the flow; see how the water is raised in that leathern bag, drawn by those receding bullocks, whose weight pressing down the inclined way, dragging away the rope, raises the bag, on which an attendant labourer, on the completion of its ascent, lays violent hands and empties its contents into a reservoir. Thus backwards and forwards do those bullocks work away, propelled on the principle of the screw, their tails being wrenched by the excited driver, whilst thwacks and imprecations fall respectively upon their backs and in their ears.

And now let us go another way. You see that long passage, with the pillars of roughest masonry, and covered and enclosed in a trelliswork of split bamboos: that is the vinery; and delicious are the grapes those vines produce. No forcing needed here—on hothouses where all is a hothouse. Then there are the melons and the cucumbers, and there are the strawberry-beds and the celery, and the spinach and the cabbage, and lettuces and potatoes. Then here are fifty different native vegetables, and there are the pomegranate, and the plantain, and the date, the citron and the orange; here are turnips and beetroot, while there is a hedge of geraniums;

and rosebushes, as you perceive, take the place of currants and of gooseberries, and are a mass of bloom, though their fragrance is but slight.

The gardener has gathered his nosegay, and the vases have been filled and tastefully arranged. And now let us stroll into the shade; and tell me if you do not think that, with all its dreary wastes, we can, by dint of perseverance, stout hearts, stout bullocks, and plenty of water, get up a very tolerable garden at "Our station."

Our Farm Yard

We have a farmyard, as a matter of course. And our every need is supplied from within the mud-walled boundaries of our grand estate. Herds and flocks, and much cattle, do we possess. We have our shepherd (that sable fellow there, carrying his almost entire wardrobe on his head, in the form of a long cloth in many folds), who tends our flock, taking them out to graze by day, and protecting them in their mud-walled fold by night. And high-caste sheep are ours, albeit they are black, and albeit they are diminutive. But, encouraged by grain, their little plump carcasses yield us delicious mutton, that a Leicester would be proud to have afforded, and a South down get emaciated on beholding. And great is the skill required to impart rotundity to the little fleecy tribe, and great is the rivalry engendered in the bosoms of our fair mistresses of the flocks, to produce the finest and the fattest in Kabob. But, coupled with the inward satisfaction of triumph, withering and sarcastic are the observations that fall upon the ear of the Coffee-shop, from those who, in all the conscious pride of furnishing the primest of the prime,

OUR GARDEN

Page No. 140

OUR FARM YARD

Page No. 144

OUR WEDDING   Page No. 14

OUR DEPARTURE FOR HOME   Page No. 1

have palmed off upon them, in return, joints microscopic and tough. But contention enters not into "our" fold, for ours is not a joint-stock association, and our meatometer does not exhibit the variations in the plate indicative of high and low feeding; for uniformity prevails, inasmuch as our flock supplies our every need.

And we cultivate cows diminutive in form, and with lacteal powers of a somewhat limited nature, but by which the sable attendants can furnish us with butter. See! there is the head slave in the very act of performing the operation. I hope you admire the simplicity of the implement. None of your grand patent American churns, or other elaborate machines, which our English dairymaids cannot do without, and who even with them so often fail to make the butter "come." Note the originality of the thing—just the identical style of contrivance made use of by Sarah of old, when she prepared butter for Abraham and his travelling guests, or, indeed, for the domestic use. A simple earthen vessel, or jar, with a stick having transverse pieces at the lower end to agitate the milk, and the motion of which is communicated by the alternate backward and forward movement of the operator's hands driving a string which moves it. Here is simplicity for you, primitive but effective and it needs it, for our "warm summer days" are not exactly calculated for the preservation of butter; and therefore its manufacture must be diurnal.

That is the herdsman who is milking the goats, of which every one keeps a flock. Indispensable are they for the supply of milk for our beverages, the flavour being so far superior to that from the cows,—useful on the line of march, too, as, after giving you your milk for the early matutinal tea, they travel on and reach the encamping-ground in time for breakfast.

Look at that individual seated in front of the kitchen door. He is cooking unfermented bread. See there, again, the simplicity of an Oriental's wants; for there before him is his kitchen range,—there is the stove, the grate, his fire—his every need. Three small heaps of clay has he rudely knocked up, and the surface has he smoothed with diluted mud; he has gathered a few sticks; he has a tin globular sort of saucepan; and with these alone is he prepared to make your bread, which, with some water and flour that he has kneaded into dough, he flattens into circular cakes with his hand, and bakes them on the bottom of his pot. There in a few minutes will he bake you unfermented cakes; and if you have good butter to spread on them, and eat them when hot, you will have no reason to complain.

This is the breakfast, the dinner, the tea, the staple food, the aliment, the nutrition, the staff of life, of millions of the indigenous, who live upon these "chupatties," which the poor eat plain, the wealthy with oil and butter, and other supplementary condiments. This is the food of the native soldiery—of high and low, of rich and poor.

Then we have our poultry-yard. But prizes for distinguished birds have not yet, although the march of intellect has stalked to Kabob, allured us to devote our talents to the improvement of the feathered tribe. We have not our Dorkings, with their exuberance of claws; we have not our Cochins, our Spanish, our Polanders, or our gold and silver spangled; but have we not our dunghill fowl, and do not the hens lay eggs that may compete in size with a hazel-nut? See! there is the guardian of our stock; for of course there is an attendant expressly devoted to this, as in poultry we have the mainstay of our existence in the East. It is the prevailing dish upon our tables, and flourishes there in endless variety,— grilled, stewed, boiled, roasted, hashed, minced, curried, cutleted, in pies, and in fifty other ways, does the everlasting chicken make its appearance. Like the "chupatty" to the native, is the chicken to the Briton; for beef is only fit for the table in the cold weather, and veal is far from attractive.

But, as the sun is getting so hot, let us leave the cattle and the poultry to their own devices, and seek the shelter of our verandah, where you can equally well digest what you have heard of the Farm Yard life at "Our Station.

Our Wedding

We all knew it would be so. Mrs. Aunks declares that she distinctly affirmed it would be a match, on the very first night that she saw Captain Cheeny talking to Carry Cinnamon at the band; and we all know how adhesive he has been to the Chutneys' carriage ever since, and how he is always to be seen sloping away to the Civil Lines at incongruous hours. Then the fact unquestionably must be true, because, when Mrs. McGhee had a vision of Barbara being married to that insane ensign who made proposals to old McGhee, she instantly got the refusal of all the orange blossoms that Pysa Doss possessed, and his are the best in the station; and, as Mrs. Chutney now wanted them, she told Pysa Doss, who announced it to Mrs. McGhee, who told Mrs. Gander, who mentioned it to Bullet (the fat wife of Corporal Bullet, who is in her service, and whom she calls her lady's-maid), who spoke of it to the ayah, who repeated it to Mrs. Gudder, who at once ordered her carriage, and paid fifteen visits that very morning, on purpose to communicate the intelligence to the whole Station.

Our weddings at Kabob have been few and far between: Ginger, our Padre, I must say, has had an easy time of it, so far as the tying of nuptial knots is concerned; and I suspect he will be glad of this event, if it is only to get rid of that detestable and everlastingly-in-the-way license which has been floating about for so many months on his library table, getting most incorrigibly mixed up with recipes for sprained ankles, receipts for resurrection stews; and sharing the cover of his domestic cookery with his own last will and testament.

But the happy day for the lovers has arrived—a "bright sunny" day, and a furious hurricane hurling its burning clouds of dust all over Kabob. The Chutneys are to give the breakfast, or, rather the dinner, for the ceremony of splicing is to be performed at dusk. The sun has betaken itself to it fiery bed. Ginger has arrived, and Cheeny and his best man, Dhalbhat, have rattled up under the portico in a state of excitement and full dress. The guests then begin to invade the church, and, martyrs to stiff-laced collars, the male species wish it was all over; while the ladies, in expectation, and with much fanning, long to see how the bride will look. The night is closing in. Ginger doubts if he will be able to see without lights; but he knows the service by heart, though not from too much practice. Cheeny has been hovering about the door, straining his eyes in the joyful direction of his coming bride, while the best man entertains serious thoughts of rushing off to see what has happened, when the rattle of carriages is heard. The long-expected ones have come, and there is the blushing Carry led up "the long-drawn aisle," supported by Chutney on her left and Cheeny on her right, and backed by her group of bridesmaids, like "clustering constellations." Letitia, and Bella, and Barbara, and Mrs. Byle's Helena—a maiden of full five summers, all decorated alike in the whitest of dresses and the bluest of et-ceteras. The bride, in the costliest of silk, with a figured lace veil that "flowed in easy negligence" from her bridal wreath, looking the very essence of a bride. There is Mrs. Chutney, and there are the Capsicums, and there is Mrs. McGhee in the everlasting pea-green, and furnished with her "new dinner set." But Ginger has commenced, and very soon are the happy pair irrevocably one. Cheeny, at the altar, is the first to salute his bride; then Mrs. Chutney showers down her kisses, and the Colonel is the first to call her "Mrs. Cheeny." Congratulations follow-the favours are bestowed—the books are signed—the happy pair drive off in the Chutneys' carriage (the coachman of which, inspired with zeal, has pinned on his favour on the very apex of his turban),—and we all disperse.

Then we take a turn on the Mall to breathe a little fresh air, display our favours to the bats. We while away an hour, until we gather again at the Chutneys. Then there is a mighty spread and grand display,—

"The polish' d marble and the shining plate;"

the table crowded, the night more sultry than ever, the punkahs drive about hot wind, and the ices relapse into tepid water. But dinner is over, the health of the happy pair is drunk right cordially, pretty things and jocose things are said, and, in spite of the heat, we are all very merry and all very gay. Then the happy pair bid us adieu, and retire. And as they are to pass their honeymoon some forty miles away, they are to perform the journey in palankeens. The torches are lit; the bride, relieved of her finery, has been packed in her case; the loving swain scrambles into his; they near the portico; we rush forth and give them a lusty cheer, as, in their palankeens "and four," they take their departure.

Then we reassemble in the drawing-room, and though the night is very hot, and "a plentiful moisture encumbers each flower" (of loveliness), we resolve to be jolly.

"Oh, what remains, what lingers yet,
To cheer us in the darkening hour?-
The *hop* remains!"

And so, with some fair ministrant at the piano, we waltz, we galope, and we polk, we flirt prodigiously with the bridesmaids, we quaff Moselle so sparkling and so bright, we feel its convivial effect, and we are so elated at beholding the happiness of the newly-married couple, that a feeling is kindled within us to fling ourselves on the knees of devotion, and resign ourselves to matrimony—and Letitia. The company, however, beginning to depart, rouses us to a sense of our danger; —

"The rattling chariots' clash, the torches'
glare,"

dispel our matrimonial illusion; but we fervently hope that the blissful pair just married will enjoy every happiness, and that we may speedily welcome them back to "Our Station."

Our Departure for Home

And so everything comes to an end. Even the long, the lingering, the dreary, and the tedious hours of an Indian day must have a close—even that fiery sun, which shot up in the vaulted arch at such small hour, and which seems to loiter on its way does at last take a downward journey, and sink to its repose—even on the sultriest of nights, when one wooes the balmy, but which will not be won, the dog that bays the moon does at last hold his peace, the jackal does eventually cease from his lamentations, the cricket from its chirrups, the bull-frogs from their croakings, and the kids from their bleatings; and though "the lingering hours prolong the night," yet even they have an ending, and the morning gun does at last boom upon the ear.

Even the reader, the gentle reader to whom we fervently hope the preceding pages have acted as the above dispellers of sleep, and who has been kept awake till now—even the reader must come to the last page and the last picture; and, to crown all, even the ten long weary years of the exile in Ind, which by the immutable laws of the empire, immutable as the

laws of the Medes and the Persians, he must pass under its
fiery sun before he can return to the fatherland—even those
ten long years do come to a close, and we find ourselves
revelling in the unutterable joy of being permitted to tear
ourselves away even from the lovely station of Kabob, that
lies so sweetly in the plains of Dekchy, in the province of
Bobarchy, and wing our way homeward from this land of the
East, from this clime of the sun, to that better land,—

> "That pale, that white-faced shore,
> Whose foot spurns back the Ocean's roaring tide,
> And coops from other lands her islanders."

And are we not in a dream—in a magnificent dream?
Are we, in sober reality, to exchange the scorched and
sunburnt plains of the lovely Kabob for the green fields
sprinkled with great white sheep? Is the cracked gong to jar
no longer on the ear, but be exchanged for the soothing
chimes of the far church bells? Are the screeching brats of
"India's supple sons" to give place to the rosy-cheeked
children, the personification of health and merriment? Are
our pale cheeks to feel the balmy air of an English winter's
day, and our fingers to feel benumbed with the frost? Are
we to taste once more of the real "roast-beef of old England,"
and our palate be gratified with really fresh oysters and
porter? Are we to hear our mother-tongue popularly spoken,
and our eyes to be gladdened with the sight of faces that are
not dusky, but that are rosy and fresh? Verily, we are; and,
in unmitigated transports of delight, we resolve upon
disposing of our worldly chattels, and making instant
preparations for departure.

Great and many have been the longings for the possession
of our choicest Arab. Many an eye has looked covetously
upon our irreproachable turn-out. That slapping mare that

trots her fourteen in the hour, and that buggy so singularly adapted for a young and blushing bride, and which the blandishments of friend Cheeny could in no wise inveigle from us. That superlatively delicious easy-chair; that immaculate spring couch; those lamps, those bookcases, those flower-vases, and the like. But we resolutely refuse to sell, and prefer to have an auction at our dwelling, when, under the presiding direction of Blades,-the comic Blades,—who is our auctioneer, a general clearance is made. Then we make straight for the office of the Kabob Tatoo Traction Company. But, inasmuch as the behaviour of the equine species had in no wise improved, and as the rival company had expended its ammunition of tatoos, we resolve to charter a vehicle to be propelled by the bipeds of the East, who in the long run—and a very good long run too—prove to be as fleet as the quadrupeds, and vastly more tractable.

Then are our stores laid in for our lengthened journey, above a thousand miles by land, before the many thousand miles at sea have to be encountered. We bid adieus—and painful adieus—to the good, kind friends who have helped to cheer full many a lingering hour during our sojourn in Kabob. And if we have a regret at "going home," it is that in all human probability we may perhaps never meet again those happy faces that ever smiled a welcome as we approached. And that although, in our future peregrinations in the West, we may make many an acquaintance—ay, and perhaps an occasional friend—we have no hopes of ever meeting with a recurrence of such friendships as we established and enjoyed in the East. But we are getting horribly sentimental; and the second bugle has sounded, and we are engaged to take our farewell dinner at the mess, which we accordingly do. The claret, more diligently cooled than ever, and the sparkling Moselle, assist to

"Speed the light convivial hour."

We drown dull care in the rosy bowl, and all that sort of thing; and eventually do we tear ourselves away, fling ourselves horizontally on the cushions of our vehicle, light our cheroot, quaff our last "peg," have our hand wrung cordially, nay, violently—our torch is lit, the team moves on, and a parting cheer vibrates in the air as we pass through the compound-gate. Then do we sedulously devote ourselves to the wooing of the balmy. The team breaks into a trot, and we whirl along; but gentle sleep sheds oblivion upon us just as, emerging on the barren plain, we take our final departure from "Our Station."